METHANE

GLOBAL WARMING

AND

PRODUCTION BY ANIMALS

by

Angela R Moss

ADAS Drayton Research Centre, Feed Evaluation Unit,
Drayton Manor Drive, Alcester Road, Stratford upon Avon,
Warwickshire, CV37 9RQ, United Kingdom

CHALCOMBE PUBLICATIONS

First published in the United Kingdom by
Chalcombe Publications,
Church Lane, Kingston, Canterbury, Kent CT4 6HX

©   Crown copyright, Ministry of Agriculture, Fisheries and
     Food 1993

ISBN 0948617 29 2

CONTENTS

PREFACE

The production of methane by microorganisms in the digestive tract of ruminant animals has been recognised for many years. It has also been recognised that this methane represents a substantial loss of potentially useful energy to the animal and an economic loss to the farmer. As a result, early studies examined the use of methane inhibiting chemicals, such as carbon tetrachloride, as dietary supplements. This work had mixed success.

The metabolisable energy system as a means of describing the energy value of ruminant feeds was introduced into the United Kingdom in the 1970s and was also adopted in modified forms in various countries around the world. This system focused attention on the need to quantify methane energy loss from particular feedstuffs, although traditional feedstuff chemistry procedures have failed to predict methane production with any accuracy.

The attention of the world in recent years has increasingly turned to the question of global warming and the potentially serious consequences it may have for future generations. Most publicity has been given to the role of carbon dioxide in this scenario. Yet, as this book has set out to show, the importance of methane as a greenhouse gas may turn out to be equally or even more important than that of carbon dioxide. This being the case, the involvement of the ruminant animal as a methane producer cannot be avoided.

Methane: global warming and production by animals is intended to bridge the gaps between nutrition, rumen microbiology and environmental science. It is hoped that the book will be a useful reference to undergraduates and postgraduate students in all of these disciplines, as well as to research workers in agriculture and environmental studies.

This book evolved from a review of knowledge commissioned by the Ministry of Agriculture, Fisheries and Food (MAFF), and funding for the work by MAFF is gratefully acknowledged.

Angela R Moss
May 1993

1

GLOSSARY

Units

g	gram
K	Kelvin scale
kcal	kilocalorie
kg	kilogram
kJ	kilojoule
km	kilometre
MJ	megajoules
mg	milligram
ml	millilitre
mV	millivolt
μm	micrometre
mol	mole (gram molecule)
nm	nanometre
%	percent
ppb	parts per billion (10^{12})
ppbv	parts per billion by volume
ppm	parts per million (10^6)
ppmv	parts per million by volume
ppt	parts per trillion (10^{18})
pptv	parts per trillion by volume
Tg	terragram (10^{12}g)

Symbols

C	carbon
Ca	calcium
CH_3	methyl radical
CH_4	methane

2

CH_3COOH	acetic acid
CH_3OH	methanol
CH_3O_2	methyl oxide radical
$CH_3(CH_2)_3COOH$	valeric acid
$CH_3(CH_2)_4COOH$	n-caproic acid
CH_3COH	acetaldehyde
$CH_3CHOHCOOH$	lactic acid
$CH_3COCOOH$	pyruvic acid
$C_2H_2(COOH)_2$	fumaric acid
$C_2H_4(COOH)_2$	succinic acid
C_2H_5OH	ethanol
C_2H_5COOH	propionic acid
C_3H_7COOH	butyric acid
CO	carbon monoxide
CO_2	carbon dioxide
$CO(NH_2)_2$	urea
Cl	chlorine ion or atom
Cl_2	chlorine
Eh	redox potential
H	hydrogen ion
H_2	hydrogen
HCl	hydrochloric acid
$HCHO$	formaldehyde
HCO_3	bicarbonate ion
H_2O	water
H_2CO_2	formic acid
HO_2	unnamed radical
HO_x	unnamed radical with x denoting the number of oxygen atoms
hv	ultra-violet radiation
K	potassium
$KHCO_3$	potassium bicarbonate
Mg	magnesium
Na	sodium
$NaHCO_3$	sodium bicarbonate

3

NH_3	ammonia
Ni	nickel
N_2	nitrogen
N_2O	nitrous oxide
NO	nitric oxide
NO_3	nitrate ion
NO_x	nitrogen oxide, with x denoting the number of oxygen atoms
O	oxygen atom
$O(^1D)$	electrically excited oxygen atom
OH	hydroxyl radical
O_2	oxygen
O_3	ozone
SO_2	sulphur dioxide
SO_3	sulphite ion
SO_4	sulphate ion

PART 1

THE ROLE OF ATMOSPHERIC

METHANE IN

GLOBAL WARMING

CHAPTER 1

GREENHOUSE GASES AND GLOBAL WARMING

Background

The physical properties which greenhouse gases have in common are that they all allow the ready penetration of solar energy to the earth's surface, but at the same time they retard the return upward flow of infra-red radiation. They combine to resist the upward flow of heat to space, hence contributing to warming the earth's surface. In fact, greenhouse gases in the atmosphere are essential for maintaining life on earth, as without them the planet would be permanently frozen because all the incoming heat from the sun would be radiated back into space by the earth's surface. The current problems which have arisen over global warming are actually due to imbalances between the increasing level of production of greenhouse gases, the slower rate of their destruction, and a relatively static requirement for them in the atmosphere, rather than to the presence of greenhouse gases *per se*.

Warming of the earth's surface is achieved by solar energy being radiated, chiefly in the visible part of the spectrum (0.4 to 0.7 μm), and passing through the atmosphere of the earth without being absorbed. Some of the solar energy is reflected back into space by clouds, and about 7% is radiated in the ultra-violet region of the spectrum (below 0.4 μm) which is absorbed by the ozone (O_3) layer in the atmosphere. The solar energy reaching the earth's surface warms the earth and is radiated back from the surface in the infra-red region of the spectrum (4 to 100 μm). Approximately 70 % of this radiation is in the wavelength band between 7 and 13 μm, which can pass back through the atmosphere into space. The remaining radiation is absorbed, essentially by water (H_2O) vapour and carbon dioxide (CO_2), thus there is warming of the lower layer of the atmosphere (troposphere), which in turn radiates heat, keeping the earth warmer than it would otherwise be (Gribbin, 1988).

As long as the amounts of water vapour and carbon dioxide in the atmosphere and the solar luminosity are constant an equilibrium is established. This equilibrium has, however, been unbalanced since the industrial age began, approximately 150 years ago. During this period it is known that concentrations of some natural trace gases in the atmosphere, such as carbon dioxide, nitrous oxide (N_2O), methane (CH_4) and tropospheric ozone have steadily increased. In addition, other gases are being emitted that are not naturally part of the global ecosystem, notably chlorofluorocarbons (CFCs). These trace gases absorb and emit radiation and are thus able to influence the earth's climate.

Identification of greenhouse gases

The realisation that the climate might change as a result of emissions of greenhouse gases into the atmosphere is not new. A British scientist, John Tyndall, published a paper in the Philosophical Magazine in 1863 about the effect of water vapour as a greenhouse gas. In the 1890s a Swede, Svante Arrhenius, indicated that the burning of fossil fuels might cause an increase in atmospheric carbon dioxide and thereby change the radiation balance of the earth. During the 1930s, Callendar (1938) for the first time convincingly showed that the atmospheric carbon dioxide concentration was increasing. The 1950s saw a revival in interest in recording atmospheric carbon dioxide concentrations and also the initiation of two observational programmes (which are still continuing), one on Mauna Loa, Hawaii and the other at the South Pole. Information from these studies showed a clear annual rhythm associated with seasonal changes in vegetation over the land masses of the Northern Hemisphere. By the 1970s it was clear that this annual cycle is superimposed on a rising trend of global mean carbon dioxide concentration (Figure 1.1). In 1957 the concentration of carbon dioxide in the atmosphere was 315 ppmv, while by 1988 it had increased to about 350 ppmv. The current atmospheric trend is an increase of 0.4% per year (1.5 ± 0.2 ppmv/year), with most of the extra carbon coming from burning fossil fuel, especially coal, and some being due to the destruction of tropical forests (Bolle, Seiler and Bolin, 1986).

As previously stated, an increase in the atmospheric carbon dioxide concentration leads to a warming of the earth's surface and lower atmosphere. In addition, a number of other greenhouse gases in the atmosphere similarly affect the radiation budget. Thus, estimated climatic effects and further impacts, such as on sea level and agriculture, must be considered to be the result of a combined effect of these potential origins of global warming.

Figure 1.1   Concentrations of atmospheric carbon dioxide observed at Mauna Loa Observatory, Hawaii.

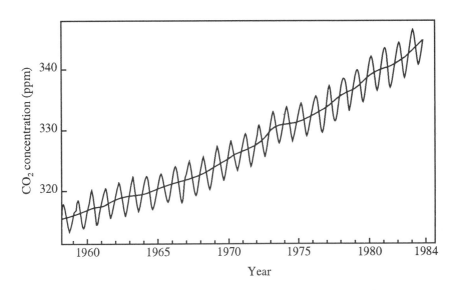

Source: After Bolle *et al* (1986).

The presence of methane in the atmosphere has been known since the 1940s, when Migeotte (1948) observed strong absorption bands in the infra-red region of the solar spectrum which were attributed to the presence of atmospheric methane. Numerous measurements since then has demonstrated the existence of an average temporal increase of atmospheric methane during the last ten years (1980 to 1990; Rodhe, 1990) of about 18 ppbv per year (1.1% per year). Information on long-term trends in methane levels has been obtained from the analysis of air bubbles trapped in the ice sheets of Greenland and Antarctica (Bolle *et al*, 1986).   Data illustrated in Figure 1.2 show relatively constant methane mixing ratios (ie concentrations) of about 0.7 ppmv before 1700 AD, but samples from polar ice cores taken in Greenland (Figures 1.2 and 1.3) show an approximately exponential increase of the tropospheric methane abundance during the last 300 years (Bolle *et al*, 1986).   This increase

9

correlates well with the increase in the human world population, which is also shown in Figure 1.3, indicating that the increase in tropospheric methane abundance is most likely to be related to anthropogenic activities, probably primarily agriculture.

Methane enters the atmosphere at or near the earth's surface after escaping from methanogenic wetland soils, rice paddies, mines, mineral exploration works, natural gas wells, transmission lines and other sources such as enteric fermentation. The total methane flux is approximately equal to 540 ($\pm$100) x 10^{12} g methane per year (Cicerone and Oremland, 1988). The large $\pm$ value reflects the large uncertainties in estimating production rates of individual ecosystems.

Figure 1.2   **Methane mixing ratios measured in air trapped in ice cores as a function of time.**

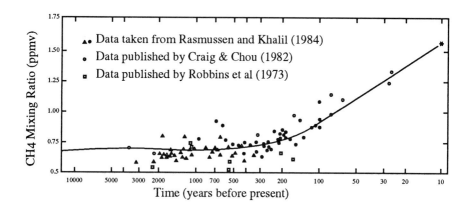

Source: After Bolle *et al*(1986).

10

An increase in tropospheric nitrous oxide abundance was first observed by Weiss (1981), who measured nitrous oxide mixing ratios in air samples collected over five years at different locations in both the Northern and Southern Hemispheres. These data showed an increase corresponding to an average annual increase of 0.2% per year. More recently, Warrick (1990) suggested an annual increase in atmospheric nitrous oxide of 0.35% per year.

Figure 1.3   **Growth of the human population and increases in atmospheric methane mixing ratios during the last 600 years, indicated by samples taken in Greenland.**

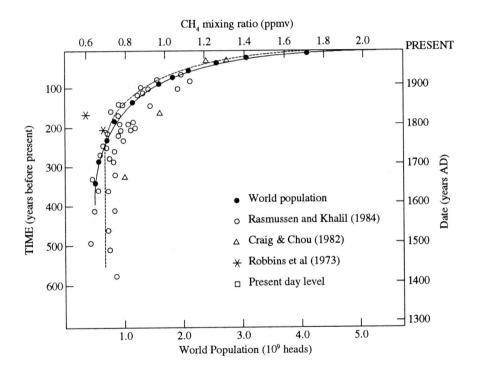

Source: After Bolle *et al* (1986).

11

The flux of nitrous oxide into the atmosphere is primarily due to microbial processes in the soil and water, which form part of the nitrogen (N_2) cycle. Nitrous oxide is also formed by nitrification in ocean water, and through anthropogenic activities such as burning fossil fuels and biomass. The total nitrous oxide flux into the atmosphere is estimated to be 12 to 15 x 10^{12} g N_2 per year (Bolle *et al*, 1986), although the contributions of different sources may be shown to be markedly different as more data become available.

The influence of increasing nitrous oxide on atmospheric chemistry appears to be restricted to the stratosphere, where it is destroyed by reaction with atomic oxygen (O). This leads to the formation of nitric oxide (NO) which reacts with stratospheric ozone, giving rise to an overall reduction of ozone abundance in the stratosphere. If present atmospheric conditions remain constant, a doubling of the nitrous oxide mixing ratio is estimated to decrease stratospheric ozone abundance by 3 to 5%.

The presence of chlorofluorocarbons in the atmosphere was detected in the early 1970s. They received considerable attention in 1974 as a possible source of chlorine (Cl_2) in the stratosphere and therefore a possible threat to the ozone layer (Molina and Rowland, 1974). Chlorofluorocarbons were also identified as a cause of enhanced atmospheric opacity, due to their infra-red absorption bands, and hence they contribute to the greenhouse effect (Ramanathan, 1975). Chlorofluorocarbons are produced for a variety of uses, such as solvents, refrigeration fluids and spray can propellants, and emissions increased rapidly from the 1940s to the 1970s. There has been a slight decline since the late 1970s, when restrictions on the use of chlorofluorocarbons were introduced in some countries.

Reactions of greenhouse gases

All the gases mentioned in this chapter interact with the radiation field of the atmosphere and hence have an effect on the climatic system. In addition, changes in the concentration of these gases and other minor atmospheric constituents can change chemical reaction rates and, accordingly, the concentrations of other gases, which may combine to influence the climate. For example, the reaction pathway for the oxidation of methane is strongly affected by the mixing ratio of nitric oxide, which is a primary pollutant. At nitric oxide mixing ratios higher than 10 pptv in the lower troposphere, the oxidation pathway of methane yields ozone molecules and hydroxyl (OH) radicals, and with an atmosphere containing less than 10 pptv nitric oxide, ozone molecules and hydroxyl radicals are destroyed by the same oxidation pathway (Crutzen, 1987). The influence of nitric oxide may lead to increasing hydroxyl and ozone concentrations in air with high nitric oxide mixing ratios (polluted atmospheres). Hydroxyl radicals are the major sink for atmospheric methane and carbon monoxide (CO), both of which have an increasing atmospheric concentration as a result of anthropogenic activities. These increases can lead to decreases in hydroxyl concentrations, thereby further increasing the carbon monoxide or methane perturbations (Chameides, Liu and Cicerone, 1977).

Methane can also react with chlorine ions (Cl) in the stratosphere, forming hydrochloric acid (HCl), which is a stable compound in the lower stratosphere. This reaction has important implications in relation to reducing the effect of active chlorine species which destroy the ozone layer.

Modelling global warming

The relative contributions of the different greenhouse gases to global warming are shown in Figure 1.4. Recent modelling work by the National Aeronautics and Space Administration (NASA) seems to indicate that temperature increases due to carbon dioxide in the atmosphere are approximately equivalent to temperature increases that would be expected from all other trace gases put together. As all trace gases, including carbon dioxide, are increasing at a rate of between 0.2% and 5% per year, important increases in world temperatures are expected early in the next century (Dowd, 1986). The connection between greenhouse gases and past global warming remains ill-defined, hence it is difficult to predict with any certainty the effects of the continued increase in greenhouse gas concentrations on global warming (Warrick and Barrow, 1990).

The analysis of likely climatic effects of increasing greenhouse gas concentrations is complex and requires the use of General Circulation Models (GCMs). These models indicate that there will be an equivalent carbon dioxide concentration doubling (to 590 ppmv) by the year 2030, which would cause the world to be approximately 1.5 to 4.5 °C warmer than today, although considering the full range of uncertainties a warming of as little as 0.5 °C or as much as 4.5 °C is possible (WMO, 1986). The concomitant rise in global mean sea level is 17 to 26 cm, with a full range of 5 to 44 cm, due principally to thermal expansion of the oceans and increased melting of small alpine glaciers (Warrick, 1990). Due to the thermal inertia of the oceans there is a

13

lag effect between global warming and a rise in sea levels. Therefore, if further increases in greenhouse gas concentrations were to stop, global warming and rises in sea levels would continue for years into the future. Transient models account for the thermal inertia of the oceans, but there are still many uncertainties and other climate variables for which the models are unable to account.

A newly developed integrated Greenhouse Gas Policy Model (GGPM) that estimates global warming from changes in gas emissions (Warrick, 1990) has been used to evaluate the climate effects of various emission control strategies. Warrick (1990) found that even stringent control strategies would do little to slow global warming by 2030, due to the lag effect of the oceans and hence the strong warming commitment already realised. However, such a strategy does have a substantial effect on warming during the second half of the 21st century.

Figure 1.4   **Relative contribution of various gases to global warming**

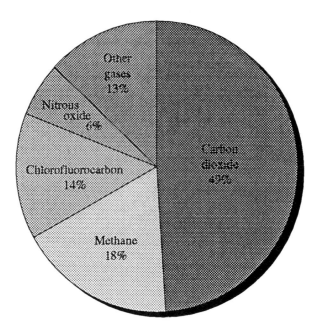

Source: After Pearce (1989)

Tropospheric concentrations and trends of the various greenhouse gases are summarised in Table 1.1.

Table 1.1   The tropospheric concentration, residence time and atmospheric trend of various greenhouse gases

Gas	Tropospheric[1] volume fraction		Tropospheric residence time[2] (years)	Atmospheric trend (%/year)
	Pre-industrial (ppmv)	1988 (ppmv)		
Carbon dioxide	280	350	~ 230	0.5
Methane	0.800	1.7	7 to 10	1.1
Nitrous oxide	0.280	0.31	170	0.35
CFC 11	0	2.6×10^{-4}	80	NA
CFC 12	0	4.4×10^{-4}	170	NA

NA Not available

CFC Chlorofluorocarbon

[1] Lowest atmospheric layer concentration

[2] Atmospheric lifetime

Source: Warrick (1990)

CHAPTER 2

METHANE AND THE ENVIRONMENT

It has been clearly established that methane is a greenhouse gas, second only in importance to carbon dioxide. Because methane is optically less thick than carbon dioxide, the greenhouse warming due to a given increase in methane concentration is greater than that for the same increase in carbon dioxide concentration. On the basis of one-dimensional radiative climate modelling (Donner and Ramanathan, 1980), the sensitivity of surface temperature to an increase in mixing ratio at present levels is about 0.2 K per ppm for methane, but only 0.006 K per ppm for carbon dioxide. Hence, if atmospheric methane and carbon dioxide concentrations continue to increase at their current respective rates, methane will fast become the most important greenhouse gas.

As methane is the most abundant organic gas in the earth's atmosphere, with recent evidence showing that atmospheric methane concentrations are increasing globally (Isaksen and Hov, 1987), it is all the more important to understand the natural processes, both biological and physical, which control atmospheric methane concentrations and to identify the human activities that are involved in methane production.

Atmospheric chemistry

The atmospheric behaviour of methane has been relatively well studied (Khalil and Rasmussen, 1983). It is a reduced gas in an oxidising atmosphere and thus must be constantly emitted by some source to be present in a steady state concentration. The chemical reactions that destructively oxidise atmospheric methane affect the chemical state of the atmosphere through the products of reactions and through the consumption of reactant species.

The most important reactant that destroys atmospheric methane is the gas phase hydroxyl radical, which is a key radical in atmospheric photochemistry. The hydroxyl radical is produced when ultra-violet radiation (hv) bombards ozone in the atmosphere in the presence of water vapour, as follows:

$$O_3 + hv \rightarrow O(^1D) + O_2 \text{ (wavelength} <315nm) \tag{1}$$

$$O(^1D) + H_2O \rightarrow 2 \text{ OH} \tag{2}$$

Only about 1% of the electronically excited oxygen atoms $(O(^1D))$ that are produced in reaction (1) react with water vapour to form hydroxyl radicals, as shown by equation (2). About 85% of atmospheric methane is destroyed by its reaction with hydroxyl radicals in the troposphere:

$$CH_4 + OH \rightarrow H_2O + CH_3 \tag{3}$$

Almost all the remaining methane is destroyed by hydroxyl ions, by chlorine atoms (Cl), and by electrically excited oxygen atoms in the stratosphere. A small proportion of methane goes through the stratosphere to the mesosphere where an additional sink, very short wavelength ultra-violet radiation, destroys methane photolytically.

Complete oxidation of methane yields carbon dioxide and water vapour:

$$CH_4 + 2O_2 \rightarrow CO_2 + 2H_2O \tag{4}$$

The actual mechanism through which the atmosphere oxidises methane is more complicated than that described in reaction (4). In fact, the mechanism of methane oxidation and the products that are formed are very different in the two cases of high or low concentrations of nitrogen oxides (NO_x). For example, the methane oxidation chain can either produce or consume ozone and hydroxyl radicals.

In air columns with high concentrations of nitrogen oxides, as occur in polluted tropospheric air and all of the stratosphere, methane oxidation produces ozone and hydroxyl radicals. The process follows four major reactions:

$$CH_4 + 4O_2 + 2hv \xrightarrow{NO\ NO_2} HCOH + H_2O + 2O_3 \tag{5}$$

$$HCOH + 4O_2 + 2hv \xrightarrow{NO\ NO_2} CO + 2O_3 + 2OH \tag{6}$$

$$HCOH + 2O_2 + hv \xrightarrow{NO\ NO_2} CO + H_2O + O_3 \tag{7}$$

$$CO + 2O_2 + hv \rightarrow CO_2 + O_3 \tag{8}$$

In equations (5), (6) and (7) nitric and nitrous oxides are catalysts, and for these pathways to proceed there must be enough nitric oxide present for the HO_2 and CH_3O_2 radicals to react preferentially with nitric oxide rather than with ozone and HO_2 radicals respectively; present rate-constant data and model results indicate that nitric oxide mole fractions must exceed 5 to 10 ppt for this to occur.

In large fractions of the troposphere nitric oxide mole fractions are probably below this level, especially in the altitude range 0 to 6 km (Ridley, Carroll and Gregory, 1987). In these conditions methane oxidation consumes ozone and HO_x species in producing carbon dioxide, water and hydrogen (H_2). Crutzen (1987) calculated in both sets of conditions the levels of ozone and hydroxyl radicals produced and consumed (high and low concentrations of nitrogen oxides respectively) when methane is oxidised to carbon dioxide and water. These are as follows for each methane molecule destroyed:

High NO_x 3.7 ozone molecules and 0.5 OH radicals are produced

Low NO_x 1.7 ozone molecules and 3.5 HO_x molecules are consumed

A potentially very important consequence of methane oxidation is that of methane, carbon monoxide and hydroxyl perturbations. As hydroxyl radicals are the major sink for atmospheric methane and carbon monoxide, and as the oxidation of these compounds to carbon dioxide tends to suppress hydroxyl concentrations there is, in principle, an instability in the system. The presence or absence of this instability is dependent on the background concentration of nitrogen oxides (Isaksen and Hov, 1987). The contemporary increase of atmospheric methane is likely to be decreasing hydroxyl concentrations, but this in turn may be causing part of the temporal increase in methane concentrations (Thompson and Cicerone, 1986). A decrease in hydroxyl concentration could be due to the increase in methane concentration or to any other factors that suppress hydroxyl levels such as an increase in carbon monoxide concentration (Cicerone, 1988). NASA's Langley Research Center recorded that there were about 25% fewer hydroxyl radicals in the lower atmosphere in 1985 than in 1950. This reduction has far reaching consequences as hydroxyl radicals remove many pollutants from the air, besides methane and carbon monoxide; for example, sulphur dioxide (SO_2), a primary pollutant, may travel further in the atmosphere before it is oxidised and falls to the ground in acid rain.

Fifteen percent of the total methane flux which is not oxidised in the troposphere enters the stratosphere, where its reaction with stratospheric hydroxyl radicals is the dominant sink, followed by reactions with electrically excited oxygen atoms and with chlorine atoms. This latter reaction (CH_4 + $Cl \rightarrow CH_3$ + HCl) is very important in stratospheric chemistry because it puts the normally ozone-destroying chlorine atoms into a form (hydrochloric acid) that is inactive towards ozone (Brasseur and Hitchman, 1988). This has important implications, as the stratospheric ozone layer is an essential natural shield which absorbs ultra-violet radiation that would otherwise reach the earth's surface.

Climatic effects

Atmospheric methane exerts an influence over the earth's climate both directly and indirectly. The more direct roles involve methane absorbing thermal infra-red radiation at about the 7.66 μm absorption band (Wang, Young, Lacis, Mo and Hansen, 1976), warming the earth's surface and the near-surface atmosphere and cooling the stratosphere; these roles are those of an effective greenhouse gas. An increase in methane concentration in the atmosphere from 0.7 ppmv (pre-industrial revolution) to its present value of about 1.7 ppmv may have caused an increase in the global temperature of the earth of about 0.23 °C (Wang et al, 1976), which is about half of the temperature increase calculated to have occurred as a result of increases in atmospheric carbon dioxide levels. Thermodynamic equilibrium calculations indicate that the equilibrium mixing ratio of methane should be about 10^{-35} (Lovelock and Margulis, 1974). The measured atmospheric mixing ratio of about 10^{-6} is a 29-order-of-magnitude enhancement due to the production of methane by biogenic processes.

The direct radiative effect of atmospheric methane also extends into the stratosphere (above 20 km) where methane molecules act to cool the atmosphere through radiative losses to space (Ramanathan, Cicerone, Singh and Kiehl, 1985).

Indirectly methane, when oxidised in the atmosphere, produces carbon monoxide which is converted further to carbon dioxide. Methane oxidation produces about 8 x 10^{14} g carbon monoxide per year (Logan, Prather, Wofsy and McElroy, 1981). Carbon monoxide molecules survive two to three months on average before conversion to carbon dioxide (via hydroxyl radicals). Hence approximately 3.4 x 10^{14} g carbon (C) per year as carbon dioxide is produced globally via this route. Total human release of carbon dioxide due to the use of fossil fuels is about 53 x 10^{14} g carbon per year (Marland and Rotty, 1984). Atmospheric production of carbon dioxide from atmospheric methane can therefore be calculated to be about 6% as much as the direct annual release of carbon dioxide from anthropogenic sources.

The oxidation of atmospheric methane in the presence of nitrogen oxides produces ozone, and if the ozone concentration increases in the upper troposphere, where ozone is a particularly effective greenhouse gas, the earth's climate will again be indirectly affected by increasing concentrations of methane. An increase in tropospheric ozone concentration has taken place at middle and high latitudes of the Northern Hemisphere during the last two to three decades (Bolle, Seiler and Bolin, 1986).

The oxidation of methane in the stratosphere provides a source of water vapour there. Increasing tropospheric methane mixing ratios will therefore give rise to higher stratospheric water vapour concentrations, which may in turn cause a temperature increase in the stratosphere due to the absorption of infra-red radiation by the water vapour.

CHAPTER 3

SOURCES AND SINKS OF METHANE

As previously stated, methane is produced by microbial activities during the mineralisation of organic carbon under strictly anaerobic conditions, such as in waterlogged soils. In addition, methane is released by anthropogenic activities such as the exploitation of natural gas, biomass burning and coal mining. Methane emission rates have been estimated by various workers over the past 30 years, with the emission rates of the individual sources reported differing by more than one order of magnitude (Table 3.1). This reflects the large uncertainties in estimating production rates. More recently, two candidate lists of annual release rates of methane sources to the atmosphere have been constructed (Table 3.2), which again emphasise the uncertainties in estimating production rates.

Table 3.1   Methane emission rates from individual ecosystems

Source	Methane emission (Tg per year)				
	Sheppard, et al (1982)	Khalil and Rasmussen (1983)	Blake (1984)	Crutzen (1985)	Seiler (1984)
Ruminants	90	120[a]	71 to 160	60	70 to 100
Paddy fields	39	95	142 to 190	120 to 200	70 to 170
Swamps/marshes	39	150	121 to 190	70 to 90	25 to 70
Ocean/lakes	65	23	18 to 34	-	15 to 35
Others: biogenic	817[b]	100[c]	60 to 397[d]	-	
Biomass burning	60	25	25 to 110	20 to 70	55 to 100
Natural gas	50	-	-	33	30 to 40
Coal mining	-	40	62 to 100	34	35
Others: nonbiogenic	50	-	-	-	1 to 2
TOTAL	1210	553	500 to 1160	400	300 to 550

[a] Including herbivorous insects

[b] Including methane production from organic solid wastes and natural ecosystems

[c] Including methane production by termites

[d] Including methane production from seasonal and tropical rain forests

23

Table 3.2   Methane emission rates from various sources

Source	Methane emission (Tg per year)		
	Cicerone and Oremland (1988)		Bouwman (1989)
	Annual release	Range	Range
Enteric fermentation	80[a]	65 to 100	66 to 90[a]
Natural wetlands	115[b]	100 to 200	40 to 160[g]
Rice paddies	110[c]	60 to 170	60 to 140[g]
Biomass burning	55[d]	50 to 100	55 to 100[h]
Termites	40	10 to 100	6 to 42[i]/2 to 5[d]
Landfills	40[e]	30 to 70	30 to 70[e]
Oceans	10[f]	5 to 20	15 to 35
Freshwaters	5[f]	1 to 25	
Methane hydrate destabilisation	5?	0 to 100 (future)	-
Coal mining	35	25 to 45	35[h]
Exploitation of natural gas	45	25 to 50	30 to 40[h]
Others: nonbiogenic	-	-	1 to 2[h]
TOTAL	540	400 to 640	338 to 714/334 to 677

[a] From Crutzen et al (1986)

[b] From Matthews and Fung (1987)

[c] From Holzapfel-Pschorn and Seiler (1986)

[d] From Crutzen (1987) and Seiler (1984)

[e] From Bingemer and Crutzen (1987)

[f] From Ehhalt (1974)

[g] From Aselmann and Crutzen (1989)

[h] From Seiler in Bolle et al (1986)

[i] From Fraser, Rasmussen, Creffield, French and Khalil (1986)

24

Not withstanding the variations in estimated values, however, in all estimates most of the biogenic methane is released by enteric fermentation, natural wetlands and rice paddies.

Methanogenesis

Methane generating (methanogenic) bacteria constitute a group of microorganisms which, along with the extremely halophilic and the thermoacidophilic bacteria, form a distinct biological kingdom known as the *Archaebacteria*. Methanogens are strict obligate anaerobes and are thus killed by exposure to air. They require highly reducing conditions (Eh = < -300mV) for growth. Hence they proliferate in aquatic sediments, flooded soils, animal gastrointestinal tracts and sewage. They also occur in extreme environments characterised by high temperatures, such as hot springs or sea floor hot vents (Ward and Olson, 1980; Anderson, Tayne and Ward, 1987), in conditions of hypersalinity and at extremes of pH. Thus these organisms have been shown to be isolated from, and active in almost any anoxic ecosystem.

Many physical, chemical and biological factors influence the physiology of methanogenic bacteria and the ecology of anaerobic ecosystems. A very significant example is temperature. Svensson (1984) reported that acetate-utilising methanogens in acidic peat soils had optimum activity at 20 $^\circ$C while hydrogen oxidisers had their optimum activity at 28 $^\circ$C. For most, if not all of the year, however, the soil did not reach the optimum temperature for either of these methanogen sub-groups. Implications of this in terms of global warming are that soils could increase in temperature, moving nearer to the optimum for the methanogens, resulting in increased methane production.

Methanogenic bacteria can metabolise only a restricted group of compounds which provide energy for their growth. Currently recognised substrates include hydrogen reduction of carbon dioxide, acetate, formate, methanol, methylated amines, carbon monoxide and dimethyl sulphide (Wolin and Miller, 1988). The majority of methanogens can grow by hydrogen reduction of carbon dioxide and some can also grow on formate. Some methanogens, for example *Methanosarcina barkeri*, can grow on almost all of these substrates, while obligately methylotrophic methanogens like *Methanococcoides methylutens* can grow only on methanol and methylated amines (Sowers and Ferry, 1983).

Methanogens are reliant upon other microorganisms to provide their required substrates. Non-methanogenic anaerobic microbes attack complex organic compounds, including biopolymers, which ultimately results in the formation of the methanogenic substrates. Interactions formed between the groups of microorganisms may be either complimentary or competitive in nature.

In complimentary interactions, fermentative organisms metabolise a given compound and the products of this metabolism are consumed by methanogens, with methane as an end product. An example of this is known as "interspecies hydrogen transfer" (Wolin, 1982).

Competitive interactions occur when two groups of microorganisms require the same substrates and hence compete for them. An example of this is the sulphate (SO_4)-reducing bacteria and methanogens, which both require hydrogen and/or acetate. Sulphate-reducing bacteria will out-compete methanogens for these substrates, and hence reduce the availability of hydrogen/acetate to methanogens (Lovley and Klug, 1983).

Methane-oxidising bacteria

Methane-oxidising bacteria (methanotrophs) oxidise methane to carbon dioxide, which both limits the flux of methane to the atmosphere from various ecosystems, such as lakes, and also removes methane from the atmosphere, as in the case of soil bacteria. Both aerobic and anaerobic bacteria are responsible for this global sink for methane.

The aerobic methanotrophs fall into two main groups, with Type 1 having "bundle disc" shaped internal membranes and utilising the ribulose monophosphate pathway for carbon assimilation. Type 2 bacteria have peripheral membranes and employ the serine pathway. Both groups oxidise methane in a sequential manner, starting with the conversion of methane to methanol (CH_3OH) by methane mono-oxygenase followed by subsequent oxidations to formaldehyde (HCHO), formic acid (H_2CO_2) and ultimately carbon dioxide. In nature, aerobic methanotrophs are generally most active in zones where both methane and oxygen (O_2) are present, that is at the interface between aerobic and anaerobic environments, such as in aerated soils, lakes and marine environments.

Anaerobic oxidation of methane is a less well understood process, but it appears to be an important methane sink in certain situations (Alperin and

Reeburgh, 1984). Most of the environments studied have been sulphate-containing systems, such as marine sediments or anoxic waters. For example, in meromictic Big Soda Lake, rates of anaerobic methane oxidation in the water column exceeded methanogenesis and at least 52% of the methane entering the water column from the bottom sediments was consumed by anaerobic oxidation, while only 0.07% and 5.2% respectively were consumed by aerobic methanotrophs or escaped to the atmosphere (Iversen, Oremland and Klug, 1987). The identification of the microorganisms involved still remains to be achieved.

CHAPTER 4

ESTIMATING METHANE EMISSIONS

Enteric fermentation

Methane is a byproduct of the microbial breakdown of carbohydrates in the digestive tracts of herbivores. This section gives an overview of enteric fermentation as a source of methane in the context of global warming, while Part 2 of this book comprises a more detailed account of methane production in the digestive tract.

Highest methane losses are reported for ruminants, which host large populations of bacteria and protozoa in their rumen (Blaxter and Czerkawski, 1966; Wolin, 1981). Published data on methane yields from different animal species have shown that it is necessary to consider different animal management and feeding schemes when calculating global methane release from domestic animals. For example, cows and sheep fed a maintenance ration showed increased methane yields with increased digestibility of the feed, but methane yields decreased when the animals were fed the same diets at 3 x maintenance (Blaxter and Clapperton, 1965). Published information concerning factors influencing ruminal methane production is, however, scarce. Crutzen, Aselmann and Seiler (1986) calculated a best estimate for methane production from enteric fermentation in ruminant animals, including all cattle, sheep and wild animals, to be 78 Tg methane per year in 1983. Factors such as variations in methane release from cattle due to differences in diet type, food consumption and age of cattle were considered by Crutzen *et al* (1986), but uncertainties remain. Methane production values by domestic animals, wild animals and humans estimated by Crutzen *et al* (1986) are shown in Table 4.1, from which it can be seen that cattle account for approximately 75% of the total methane produced from enteric fermentation.

The global production of methane from wild ruminants is difficult to estimate due to lack of sufficient data on animal populations, feed types and feed intakes.

Table 4.1   Global methane production by domestic animals, humans and wild ruminants

Animal type and region of the world	Population $(\times 10^6)$	Mean gross energy intake (MJ/day)	Methane energy loss (% of gross energy intake)	Methane production (kg/animal /year)	Methane production by total population (Tg/year)
Cattle					
Developed countries +	572.6	126	6.65	55	31.5
Brazil and Argentina Developing countries	652.8	60.3	9.00	35	22.8
Buffalos	124.1	85	9.00	50	6.2
Sheep					
Developed countries	399.7	20	6.00	8	3.2
Developing countries and Australia	737.6	13	6.00	5	3.7
Goats	476.1	14	5.50	5	2.4
Camels	17.0	100	9.00	59	1.0
Pigs					
Developed countries	328.8	38	0.60	1.5	0.5
Developing countries	444.8	12.7	1.20	1.0	0.4
Horses	64.2	110	2.50	18.0	1.2
Mules, asses	53.9	61	2.50	10.0	0.5
Humans	4669.7	-	-	0.05	0.2
Moose, elk	0.85	53	9.00	31.0	0.03
Large deer	22.0	26	9.00	15.0	0.33
Roe deer	4.0	5	9.00	3.0	0.01
TOTAL					73.97

Source: Crutzen *et al* (1986)

Table 4.2   Methane production by wild animals in the Serengeti

Species	Population $(\times 10^4)$	Mean gross energy intake (MJ/day)	Methane energy loss (% of gross energy intake)	Methane production (kg/animal /year)	Methane production by total population (Tg/year)
Ruminants					
Wildebeest	72	22	9.0	13	0.0094
Buffalo	10.8	57	9.0	34	0.0037
Thompson's gazelle	98.1	4	9.0	2	0.0020
Giraffe	1.7	84	9.0	50	0.0008
Eland	2.4	46	9.0	27	0.0006
Topi	5.6	19	9.0	11	0.0006
Impala	11.9	9	9.0	5	0.0006
Kongoni	2.1	22	9.0	13	0.0003
Waterbuck	0.3	26	9.0	15	0.0001
Grant's gazelle	0.6	9	9.0	5	<0.0001
Non-ruminants					
Zebra	0.240	31	2.5	5	0.00120
Elephant	0.005	157	2.5	26	0.00013
Warthog	0.034	10	2.5	1	0.00003
Hippopotamus	0.002	104	2.5	17	0.00003
Rhinoceros	0.001	90	2.5	15	0.00002
TOTAL					**0.01951**

Source: Crutzen *et al* (1986)

31

Table 4.2 summarises information on populations and mean body weights of wild ruminants in the Serengeti (Houston, 1979). Assuming this methane production to be representative of global conditions, total methane production by the wild ruminant population of 200 to 600 million, may be equal to 2 to 6 Tg per year, which is a very small amount compared to methane production by domestic animals.

Estimated methane production by domestic animals, humans and wild ruminants in the UK is shown in Table 4.3. Approximately 1.4 Tg methane is produced per year, which accounts for about 2% of world methane production by enteric fermentation. This UK production is a very small proportion of the world figure but 95% of it is from domestic animals whose feeding regimes could be manipulated.

It is estimated that in recent years the rate of increase of methane released from domestic ruminants (mainly cattle and sheep) has been about 1% per year (Crutzen et al, 1986), equivalent to approximately 1 Tg per year. Further work is needed, however, to establish more confidence in the methane yields adopted, taking into account factors such as diet types, diet interactions and feed intakes. Similarly animal population data need to be verified and improved.

Natural wetlands

To calculate methane production from natural wetlands, the major wetland groups must be established by studying wetland types, areas and ecological classification schemes. Matthews and Fung (1987) distinguished five types of wetlands, namely forested and non-forested bogs, forested and non-forested swamps and alluvial formations. Aselmann and Crutzen (1989) distinguished the following six types of natural wetlands, including lakes: bogs, fens, swamps, marshes, floodplains and shallow lakes. The total area corresponds well between the two estimates, although regional disagreement between the data suggests that present knowledge of wetlands is still incomplete. Parts of the wetlands are only temporarily flooded and are therefore only active in methanogenesis during part of the year, with the duration and extent of flooding being dependent on prevailing climatic and hydrological conditions. Considerable portions of the marshes may consist of unvegetated open waters, which have lower methane emission rates than vegetated areas (Cicerone, Shetter and Delwiche, 1983).

Table 4.3 **Methane production by domestic animals, humans and wild ruminants in the UK**

Animal type	Population[1] (x10^6)	Mean gross energy intake[2] (MJ/day)	Methane energy loss[2] (% of gross energy intake)	Methane production (kg/animal /year)	Methane production by total population (Tg/year)
Dairy cows	3.036	241	8	126	0.38
Beef cows	1.339	174	8	91	0.12
Heifers	0.772	114	8	60	0.046
Other cattle	7.035	109	8	57	0.40
Ewes	14.789	20	8	10.5	0.16
Shearlings	3.267	20	8	10.5	0.034
Other sheep	20.732	17.3	8	9.1	0.19
Goats	0.150	14	7.5	6.9	0.001
Sows	0.813	54.8	0.8	2.9	0.002
Gilts	0.105	39.8	0.8	2.1	0.0002
Growing pigs	6.988	39.8	0.8	2.1	0.015
Pullets	18.627	10.6	0.3	0.21	0.004
Laying hens	38.182	13.3	0.3	0.26	0.010
Broilers	67.444	18.6	0.3	0.37	0.025
Deer	0.500	18	8.0	9.44	0.005
Horses	0.500	167	5	55	0.028
Humans	57.000	-	-	0.05	0.003
TOTAL					1.4232

[1] From MAFF (1989)

[2] From Crutzen et al (1986)

Recent global flux estimates for natural wetlands are 115 Tg per year (Matthews and Fung, 1987) and 40 to 160 Tg per year (Aselmann and Crutzen, 1989), as shown in Table 3.2. This wetland source may change if estimates of geographic extents of different types of natural wetlands improve and the number of flux measurements increases, particularly in undersampled regions. It has been suggested that future global warming in northern areas may increase flux rates from natural wetlands considerably due to increased phytomass production and accelerated fermentation (Bouwman, 1989).

Rice paddies

Rice paddies appear in Table 3.2 as a major methane source. The potential for methane release from rice fields has been noted for a number of years (eg Koyama, 1964; Ehhalt, 1974), but no field measurements were reported before those of Cicerone and Shetter (1981), who discovered the importance of methane transport through the aerenchyma system of the plants, as opposed to diffusion and bubble transport across the water-air interface. Seiler (1984) suggested that more than 95% of the total methane released from paddy soils is from diffusive transport through the plants and not through diffusion or the escape of bubbles across the air-water interface. Transport of methane from paddy soils into the atmosphere by the latter method is only important for unplanted fields. Holzapfel-Pschorn and Seiler (1986) reported that rice plants, but not weeds have a stimulatory effect on methane emission and that rice paddies emit about twice as much methane as unplanted fields.

Many factors control or influence methane production and release rates during the growing of rice. These include agricultural practices, time of the season, irrigation and both physical and chemical soil properties. For example, *in situ* experiments by Holzapfel-Pschorn and Seiler (1986) and Seiler, Holzapfel-Pschorn, Conrad and Scharffe (1984) in Italian and Spanish rice paddies respectively gave methane emissions of 27 to 81 g per square metre and 12 g per square metre over the growing season. The low estimate for the Spanish rice paddy was attributed to an inflow of sulphate-containing Mediterranean water which would have inhibited methanogenesis.

Further uncertainties in the estimation of methane production arise because about 95% of the world's harvested area of paddy rice is located in the Far East, from where data on methane emission rates are not yet available. All of these factors make the extrapolation of emission rates from published individual studies to a global scale very difficult and possibly imprecise.

The effective area of land used for rice growing is increasing with time, partly due to multiple cropping which is permitted by irrigation and partly due to cultivation of new land areas. Holzapfel-Pschorn and Seiler (1986) have estimated that the harvested area of paddy rice has increased at an annual rate of 1.6% since about 1940. It is uncertain whether the total methane flux from rice paddies will have increased proportionately, as the rice paddy area may be split into rain-fed and irrigated areas. Considerable areas of rain-fed rice have deep and intermediate water depths, where methane release rates are much lower than those for the well-managed shallow rice paddies.

Biomass burning

One of the major sources of abiogenic methane is the burning of biomass material such as during the disposal of agricultural wastes, savanna fires, and shifting cultivation practices. Estimates to date have recognised large uncertainties and sources of variability, such as types of burning, moisture content of the vegetation and amounts of biomass that are burned annually. As with many processes, it is important to measure the ratios of methane to carbon dioxide and of methane to total carbon burned, and more accurate estimates will require a great deal of experimental work. It is widely believed that increased rates of forest clearing by burning are contributing to the increase in methane emission due to biomass burning, but there appear to be no quantitative data to confirm this apparent trend.

Termites

Various researchers have estimated methane production from termites using different species under laboratory conditions. Results have been very different. A first estimate of the potential production of methane by termites was made by Zimmermann, Greenberg, Wandiga and Crutzen (1982), which suggested an annual production of 150 Tg methane per year. At the lower end of the range, however, Seiler, Conrad and Scharffe (1984) reported methane production by termites of only 2 to 5 Tg methane per year. The highest values for termite methane production may be considerably overestimated and the low figures (Seiler, 1984; Collins and Wood, 1984; Fraser et al, 1986) are probably more realistic.

Collins and Wood (1984) stated that the sub-family of *Macrotermitinae* (fungus growing termites) is dominant in many ecosystems of the Ethiopian and Indo-Malayan regions and, since most of their digestion is performed aerobically by fungi, members of this sub-family are unlikely to produce much methane. Soil feeders, which occur in most tropical regions, use degraded soil organic matter and hence, if methane is produced, it is likely to be in small amounts. In addition air turbulence occurring during laboratory measurements is known to cause increased termite activity, with higher carbon dioxide and probably methane production.

In order to quantify termites as a source of methane production more accurately, difficult ecological evaluations are required. For example, termite populations, amounts of organic material consumed by termites in various biomasses, species differences, and the activity of methane-oxidising bacteria occurring in the soil of termite mounds must be determined.

Landfills and animal wastes

Anaerobic decay of organic wastes in landfills and dumps has increased in recent years, with very large increases expected in the coming decades from the developing world (Bingemer and Crutzen, 1987). In Britain, methane from several tips is already tapped and burnt as fuel. A recent estimate put the escape of methane from landfill sites in Britain each year at 2.2 Tg per year (Pearce, 1989). The estimates range widely and more information is required in several areas, such as the amounts and types of waste materials, trends in landfill practices (for example shredding and covering), the age of the site, the role of methane oxidisers, and methane burning. Reduction of emissions from landfills may be achieved by gas harvesting or by recycling of solid wastes (Bouwman, 1990).

There is little information on the anaerobic decay of animal wastes, although it is assumed that farmyard manure usually composts to carbon dioxide and water, whereas stored slurry from housed animals requires anaerobic conditions for methane production. The anaerobic decay of slurries is slow and methanogenic activity may be inhibited at low temperatures and in the presence of aeration units. Livestock wastes are a potentially large source of methane emission, particularly in developed countries where large proportions of livestock are intensively housed. Global methane emissions from animal waste have been estimated at 28 Tg per year, ranging from 20 to 35 Tg per year (Safley, Casada, Woodbury and Roos, 1992). These estimates are very uncertain due to insufficient data on animal numbers, sizes and feeding regimes, and to limited data on the methane producing potential of animal wastes under various waste management systems. This source of methane therefore warrants further investigation into levels of methane emission, and management techniques to reduce these levels.

Oceans and freshwaters

Early work indicated that the surface waters of the world's ocean represented only a minor source of methane to the atmosphere. Oremland (1979) suggested that methanogenesis occurs within the anaerobic gastrointestinal tracts of marine zooplankton and fish. It is likely that the rate of methane production varies from open ocean areas and from coastal regions, where it is hypothesised that rates are increased due to methane from sediments and drainage. To achieve a more accurate estimate of oceanic methane production extensive sampling of marine surface waters would be necessary, particularly near-shore and shelf waters, with attention to seasonal variation. Freshwaters have received little attention, hence large uncertainties surround current estimates of methane production.

Methane hydrates

Methane hydrates are solid structures composed of rigid cages of water molecules that surround methane molecules. The pressure and temperature regime for stability and other factors imply that these hydrates are most prevalent at depth under permafrost and beneath the sea on continental margins (Kvenvolden, 1989). If warmer waters penetrate to the bottom of the oceans or a warmer climate penetrates the permafrost, the methane held in hydrates may be released. Many factors control the amounts of methane that could be released, including the environmental distribution and origins of hydrates and thus the amounts of gas in the hydrates, and the fractions of all the hydrates that are located in layers and in stable thermal environments that are insulated from climatic change. There is some evidence that hydrates in coastal permafrosts are decomposing, although present annual release rates have not been estimated.

Potential methane release from these hydrates is considered to be very great, and this methane source could become of major importance. The hydrates should be monitored closely as melting permafrosts could be an early indication of global warming.

Coal mining and natural gas production

There are very few published data on methane release from coal mining operations, natural gas exploration and transmission, oil exploration, venting gas wells and explosive events. Much work is required to quantify these losses, in view of increases in methane released from coal mining and increased natural gas usage in recent years.

PART 2

METHANE FROM ANIMALS

CHAPTER 5

ENTERIC FERMENTATION

Digestion

The majority of feeds ingested by herbivorous mammals are high in structural carbohydrates (principle components of the cell walls). These carbohydrates are mainly cellulose and hemicellulose. No herbivorous mammals have the ability to digest these polysaccharides, but many prokaryotic and eukaryotic microorganisms synthesise enzyme complexes capable of degrading them (Hungate, 1966). All mammals that are primarily herbivorous have evolved a digestive system whereby they can utilise cell wall components by means of a symbiotic association with microorganisms capable of digesting these polysaccharides. The microorganisms are contained in an expanded part of the alimentary tract where bulky fibrous foods, rich in cellulose and other polysaccharides, can be delayed in passage to allow extensive microbial fermentation to take place. The expanded portion of the alimentary tract may be either anterior to the abomasum (foregut fermentation) as in ruminants, colobid monkeys, hippopotami and camels, or posterior to the abomasum (hindgut fermentation) as in horses, elephants and some rodents (Church, 1973).

Ruminants ingest plant polymers, for example in grasses, hay, silage and cereals, which undergo preliminary processing in the oral cavity. This consists mainly of comminution of the food by mastication, and mixing with copious amounts of saliva. The plant material is then swallowed and passes into the reticulo-rumen (generally termed the rumen), which represents about 85% of the total stomach capacity and contains digesta equal to about 10 to 20% of the animal's weight; the rumen capacity of adult sheep is some 6 to 10 litres and that of cattle 100 to 130 litres (Annison and Lewis, 1959). This large organ satisfies the requirements for life of most ruminant animals by allowing food to be consumed quickly and digested slowly. Semi-digested fibrous food can reside for long periods in the rumen and, additionally, the solid digesta may be regurgitated and rechewed during periods when the animal is not eating and is safe from predators. Much information on the physiology and structure of the ruminant alimentary canal can be found in Church (1973).

In the rumen a massive community of microorganisms ferments plant material in order to obtain energy and carbon for its own growth and division. Carbohydrates are fermented, lipids and proteins are hydrolysed and some of the products are utilised by the microorganisms themselves. The net result is that little dietary soluble carbohydrate or soluble protein enters the true stomach (the abomasum), and short-chain volatile fatty acids (VFAs), methane and carbon dioxide are the main end-products of the microbial fermentation, together with microbial material. The VFAs are removed by absorption through the rumen wall into the bloodstream and are subsequently used as the ruminant's primary source of energy and carbon. The gases produced are waste products of the fermentation and are removed by eructation. Microorganisms, small undigested food particles and substances in solution are semi-continuously removed from the rumen into the abomasum, then they pass to the lower part of the digestive tract (small and large intestines).

The digestive processes which occur subsequent to the rumen are similar to those of monogastric animals. Digestion of the microbial mass exiting from the rumen provides the animal with its major source of amino acids, vitamins and minerals. Any substrates unavailable to animal digestive enzymes arriving at the hind gut (colon and caecum) along with secretions of saliva and mucus may undergo further fermentation by the microbial population inhabiting this part of the digestive tract. VFAs are the end-products of fermentation and are removed by absorption through the gut wall. Undigested microbial and feed residues, and microorganisms that inhabit the large intestine leave the animal in the faeces.

The rumen environment

The rumen can be likened to a highly efficient semi-continuous fermentation apparatus but it differs from man-made fermentation equipment in several ways. The inner epithelial wall of the rumen is semi-permeable and selectively transports small molecules to and from the animal's bloodstream. For example, VFAs are transported from the rumen to the blood, and bicarbonate (HCO_3) ions are transported in the reverse direction. Neurol responses to specific stimuli activate physiological mechanisms for eructation, activate contractions to mix and move rumen contents and activate the mechanism for

42

regurgitation of solids. The biological features of the rumen provide mechanisms for the fermentation of solid substrates, for product removal, for maintenance of pH and for the disposal of fermentation gases (Church, 1973).

The rumen is a warm ($39^{o}C$), anaerobic, chemically-reducing (oxidation - reduction potential about -350 mV) environment rich in organic matter. From the microbiological standpoint it may be considered as three interconnecting environments: the liquid phase, the solid phase and the rumen epithelium. Overlying the rumen contents is the gaseous phase which essentially consists of carbon dioxide and methane, although trace amounts of other gases such as hydrogen, nitrogen and oxygen, have been reported. The production of gases is rapid and the mixture consists of approximately 65% carbon dioxide and 35% methane, with methane arising strictly as a fermentation product. Carbon dioxide is produced both from fermentation and by neutralisation of acids by bicarbonate ions from saliva and the bloodstream.

The pH of the rumen contents is approximately pH 6.5. This is held relatively constant by the buffering actions of the large amount of saliva which is secreted and which is high in sodium and potassium bicarbonate ($NaHCO_3$ and $KHCO_3$) and urea ($CO(NH_2)_2$). Buffering is also maintained by absorption of VFAs produced through the rumen wall into the bloodstream, and by ammonia (NH_3) produced during the fermentation (Church, 1973).

The parameters of the rumen environment impose some obvious constraints on the microbial populations expected in the ecosystem. Dominant species have to be either facultative anaerobes or anaerobes, with obligate aerobes existing in very low concentrations. The rumen dilution rate also sets some approximate upper limits on the generation times of organisms that can be maintained in the ecosystem. Different microorganisms are associated with the different phases in the rumen. The liquid phase of the rumen fluid has been examined more extensively, both microbiologically and chemically, than the solid phase or the rumen epithelium. However, it is in the digesta that the most significant reactions, concerned with the digestion of cell walls, occur. Many rumen bacteria are associated with the digesta (Cheng, Akin and Costerton, 1977), as are phycomycete fungi (Bauchop, 1979) and, at times, a significant proportion of the ciliate protozoa population (Orpin, 1979). The bacteria associated with the digesta may be more than twice as numerous as in the fluid phase (Warner, 1962) and about half the total bacterial population (Weller, Gray and Pilgrim, 1958). The rumen epithelium also supports a population of adherent bacteria (Cheng, McCowan and Costerton, 1979).

The turnover time for the solid phase is longer than that for particles in the liquid phase, about 1 to 2 days compared with 0.3 to 0.8 days (Hungate, 1966). Hence, microorganisms associated with the solid phase with generation times of about two days or less would not be washed out of the rumen. If the rumen was a homogeneously mixed reactor with a turnover time of 0.7 days, the protozoa and much of the bacterial population would not be able to remain in the rumen. It is the stratification of the rumen contents that allows microbial populations with a range of generation times to survive. The methane-forming bacteria have relatively long generation times but remain in the system because the dilution rate can accommodate this. Much longer rumen turnover times, of 5 to 10 days, would encourage the development of bacteria that could participate in complete bioconversion of organic carbon to methane and carbon dioxide, as occurs in waste disposal systems. This would limit the sources of carbon and energy required by the animal's metabolism and would thus be detrimental to it. Hence the environment and microbial population of the rumen reflect the evolution of the most efficient symbiotic system.

Rumen microbiology

The rumen contains a very varied, complex and dense population of microorganisms, which may be considered as three main groups: bacteria, protozoa and fungi. The majority of the dominant microorganisms are obligate anaerobes found in no other habitats, but facultatively anaerobic bacteria are also present and may play a significant role in reactions on the rumen epithelium (Wallace, Cheng, Dinsdale and Ørskov, 1979). Their ability to scavenge oxygen from the system which might otherwise limit the growth of the obligate anaerobes may be their major role in the rumen ecology.

The numbers of all rumen microorganisms vary between animals and fluctuate with time after feeding, and the diet and health of the animal (Hungate, 1966). The majority of estimates of microbial population size have been carried out using filtered rumen contents, which are not strictly representative of the rumen in its entirety as many microorganisms live within the solid matrix of digesta or are associated with the epithelium. The counts that have been made suggest the bacteria are normally present at 1×10^{10} to 1×10^{11} per ml, the ciliate protozoa at 1×10^4 to 1×10^6 per ml and flagellate protozoa at 1×10^3 to 1×10^5 per ml. Approximately 200 species of bacteria and more than 20 species of protozoa have been identified to date. A review of the physiology of rumen microorganisms can be found in Hungate (1966) and their biochemical activities are detailed in Prins (1977).

Many interrelationships exist between rumen microorganisms. Readily metabolisable plant constituents such as soluble sugars and proteins disappear from the digesta shortly after it enters the rumen (Hungate, 1966), leaving the more slowly digested plant cell walls as the major component of the digesta. As only a few of the rumen microorganisms are cellulolytic, many of the other microorganisms rely on the release of nutrients or fermentation products from the cellulolysis of the plant cell walls for their substrates. Some of the end products of fermentation of important substrates by selected rumen microorganisms are summarised in Table 5.1, from which it can be seen that the *Methanobacterium* bacteria are the only microorganisms to produce methane as the end product of fermentation.

Hindgut fermentation

Hindgut fermentation takes place in ruminants as well as in monogastric animals. The importance of hindgut fermentation has often been under-estimated, as indicated by the relative proportions of the hindgut to the total body weight (Demeyer, 1988). In sheep, hindgut fermentation may become important with diets of low digestibility (Ulyatt, Bellow, Reid and Bauchop, 1975).

There is a similarity between the rumen and hindgut in the identity of the major fermentation end products (acetic (CH_3COOH), propionic (C_2H_5COOH) and butyric (C_3H_7COOH) acids), present in roughly the same proportions in both areas. Lower production of methane in the hindgut has been shown by De Graeve and Demeyer (1988). End products of fermentation in rumen contents obey the proposed stoichiometric equation for the fermentation of hexose units (Demeyer and Van Nevel, 1975) and hydrogen recovery from the end-products of rumen fermentation yields values between 80 and 90% (Marty and Demeyer, 1973). Hydrogen recoveries for hindgut fermentation never exceed 70%. De Graeve and Demeyer (1988) found higher proportions of propionate in the hindgut compared with the rumen, but insufficient to compensate for the lower hydrogen recoveries, suggesting that, besides methane, other potential hydrogen-sink reactions must exist.

45

An alternative hydrogen-sink reaction is acetogenesis from carbon dioxide via the following reaction:

$$4H_2 + 2CO_2 \rightarrow CH_3COOH + 2H_2O$$

This reaction has been observed in the hindgut of non-ruminants (Prins and Lankhorst, 1977). De Graeve and Demeyer (1988) carried out a series of experiments *in vitro* in order to obtain evidence of such a reaction occurring in hindgut fermentation as opposed to rumen fermentation. The experiments indicated that hindgut fermentation produced acetic acid through reduction of carbon dioxide with hydrogen; this did not occur in the rumen.

Table 5.1   Fermentation products and energy sources of important rumen microorganisms

Substrate:	Cellulose		Starch			Pectin		Simple sugars (lactate)		Formate (H$_2$+CO$_2$)
Microorganisms:	Bacteroides succinogenes	Ruminococcus	Bacteroides amylophilus	Succinomonas amylolytica	Entodinium	Lachnospira	Eubacterium	Pentostreptococcus elsddenii	Holotricha	Methanobacterium
End product										
Volatile fatty acids										
Acetate	*	*	*	*	*	*	*	*	*	
Propionate				*	*			*	*	
Butyrate					*		*	*	*	
Other acids										
Formate	*	*			*	*	*			
Lactate		*	*			*				
Succinate	*	*	*	*					*	
Ethanol		*	*			*				
Gases										
Hydrogen	*	*				*	*	*	*	
Carbon dioxide					*	*	*	*	*	
Methane										*

Source: Czerkawski (1986)

47

CHAPTER 6

METHANE BACTERIA

Methane generating (methanogenic) bacteria constitute a group of microorganisms, which along with the extreme halophilic and the thermoacidophilic bacteria, form a distinct biological kingdom known as the *Archaebacteria*. Methanogens are strict obligate anaerobes and are thus killed by exposure to oxygen. Within the past twenty years, studies have established the widespread and fundamental role of the methane-producing bacteria in anaerobic degradation processes in nature (Mah, Ward, Baresi and Glass, 1977). More elusive has been an understanding of the systematic relationships among the methane bacteria and their relationship to other procaryotes.

The methanogens are a morphologically diverse group of organisms, but they are a physiologically coherent group of strict anaerobes, sharing the common metabolic capacity to produce methane. Early taxonomic schemes dispersed the methanogenic bacteria among the better characterised bacterial groups according to their morphologies. Phylogenetic analysis based on ribosomal ribonucleic acid (RNA) sequence characterisation has more recently placed the methanogens in the aforementioned distinct grouping of *Archaebacteria* (Balch, Fox, Magnum, Woese and Wolfe, 1979). This group is separate from both the eubacterial urkingdom (composed of the 'typical bacteria') and the urkaryotic urkingdom (representing the cytoplasmic component of eukaryotic cells). Methanogens share with the eubacteria features such as a similar size, absence of cellular organelles and ribosomal subunit sizes. Features in common with urkaryotes include insensitivity to vancomycin, penicillin and kanamycin, absence of formyl-methionine in protein synthesis and adenosine diphosphate (ADP)-ribosylation of the peptide elongation factor EF2 by diphtheria toxin (Daniels, Sparling and Dennis Sprott, 1984).

Apart from ribosomal RNA sequence homology, other important distinctly archaebacterial features include: ether-linked proty-isoprenoid glycerol lipids as opposed to ester-linked alkanelipids; non-peptidoglycan cell walls of various types containing peptides and/or carbohydrates; absence of thymidine in the 'common arm' of the transfer RNA; absence of dihydrouracil and distinct transcription systems (Daniels *et al*, 1984). RNA translation too is distinctive and the shape of the ribosome itself is different from that in the other two urkingdoms.

The methanogens form a diverse group of organisms which currently comprises the following 12 genera:

> *Methanobacterium* (Mb.)
> *Methanobrevibacterium* (Mbr.)
> *Methanogenium* (Mg.)
> *Methanospirillum* (Msp.)
> *Methanosarcina* (Ms.)
> *Methanococcus* (Mc.)
> *Methanothrix* (Mtx.)
> *Methanoplanus* (Mpl.)
> *Methanothermus* (Mt.)
> *Methanolobus* (Ml.)
> *Methanococoides* (Mcc.)
> *Methanomicrobium* (Mmb.)

Of these, the methanogens that have been isolated from the rumen include *Mb. formicicum* (Oppermann, 1957) and *Mbr. ruminantium* (Smith and Hungate, 1958) which belong to the order *Methanobacteriaceae*. *Methanomicrobium mobile* (Paynter and Hungate, 1968), *Ms. barkeri* and *Ms. mazei* belong to the order *Methanomicrobiaceae*. The bacteria assumed to play the most significant roles in ruminal methanogenesis are *Mbr. ruminantium* and *Methanosarcina* isolates similar to *Ms. barkeri*. However, new types continue to be isolated, and the relative importance of existing known species may be altered. Miller, Wolin, Hongxue and Bryant (1986) isolated both coenzyme M-requiring and -non-requiring *Methanobrevibacter* strains in high concentrations (10^8 to 10^9 per ml) from the bovine rumen. Two of these strains required a fatty acid mixture for growth (isobutyric, isovaleric, 2-methylbutyric and valeric acids), whilst the other strains were stimulated by this mixture, but it was not essential.

Methanobrevibacter ruminantium

This species was first described by Smith and Hungate (1958) as a *Methanobacterium*, *Mb. ruminantium*, which consists of short, non-motile,

50

Gram-positive coccobacilli about 0.7μm wide and up to 1.8μm in length. The major substrate is hydrogen/carbon dioxide, but formate can be used when it is present at concentrations higher than those in the rumen (Hungate, Smith, Bauchop, Yu and Rabinowitz, 1970). Like the cell walls of other methanogens, those of *Mbr. ruminantium* lack peptidoglycan. The major cell envelope component (pseudomurein), differs from eubacterial murein in several respects (Jones, Nagle and Whitman, 1987). The absence of peptidoglycan makes these bacteria insensitive to antibiotics that inhibit its synthesis; even chloramphenicol, which inhibits protein synthesis in eubacteria, differs in its mode of action against some methanogens (Harris, Evans, Knox and Archer, 1987).

Methanosarcina barkeri

Most isolates of *Ms. barkeri* have been obtained from mud and anaerobic digesters, although Beijer (1952) reported the presence of acetate-utilising *Methanosarcina* in the rumen of a goat. When Rowe, Loughnan, Nolan and Leng, (1979) fed sheep on a diet rich in molasses the numbers of *Methanosarcina* in the rumen reached 10^9 per ml. Patterson and Hespell (1979) detected *Methanosarcina* at about 10^5 to 10^6 per ml in the rumen of cattle fed lucerne, maize and soyabean meal.

The cells are Gram-positive, non-motile spheres, 1.5 to 2.0μm in diameter, which occur in large clusters. Substrates for methane formation include hydrogen/carbon dioxide, methanol (CH_3OH), methylamines (formed in the rumen from the breakdown of choline; Patterson and Hespell, 1979) and acetate moieties. Like other methanogens, the cell envelopes of *Ms. barkeri* lack peptidoglycan, but the major polymer differs from that present in *Methanobrevibacter*, and consists of heteropolysaccharides (Jones *et al*, 1987).

CHAPTER 7

BIOCHEMISTRY OF METHANE PRODUCTION

Two major pathways are used in nature for the formation of methane. One involves the reduction of carbon dioxide by hydrogen, and the other involves the decarboxylation of acetate to methane and bicarbonate. Methane is produced from the methyl group of acetate by the latter pathway, and carbon dioxide is not reduced. The contributions of carbon dioxide reduction by hydrogen and acetate decarboxylation to methanogenesis in an ecosystem can be determined by measuring the amount of methane formed from radioactive carbon dioxide and the amount formed from radioactive methyl-labelled acetate. Labelling studies in the rumen show that the majority of methane is produced by reduction of carbon dioxide (Mah et al, 1977).

Thus rumen methanogenic bacteria use hydrogen and carbon dioxide to form methane. The amount of hydrogen used is 4 mol per mol of methane produced and the change in free energy for this reaction is -134kJ per mol methane. Assuming that about -37 kJ per mol of energy is needed to produce one mol of adenosine triphosphate (ATP) (Thauer, Jungermann and Decker, 1977), a minimum of 3 mols ATP per mol of methane would be evolved from the reduction of carbon dioxide by hydrogen.

Knowledge of the pathways involved in methanogenesis is far from complete, although it is increasing. The scheme of methanogenesis described in Figure 7.1 depicts the most recent developments in methanogenesis research (Daniels et al, 1984). The major coenzymes believed to be involved in the methanogenesis pathway are described in the following sections.

Carbon transfer

Coenzyme M (2-mercaptoethanesulphonic acid)

Coenzyme M was the first novel cofactor described in the methanogens and it has not been found in any other organisms (Balch and Wolfe, 1979). The mercapto end carries a methyl group in the last two-electron reduction step in methanogenesis. This reaction is catalysed by CH_3-S-CoM reductase. It has been proposed that coenzyme M is somehow attached to factor F_{430} of the methyl reductase enzyme-forming coenzyme MF_{430} which plays a key role in methane formation. Work by Huster, Gilles and Thauer (1985) has shown that F_{430} and CoM extracted from *Mbr. ruminantium* can easily be separated. Thus, if in *Mbr. ruminantium* CoMSH and F_{430} are associated with each other, then this is not via a covalent bond. The structural and functional relationship between these two coenzymes is unknown.

Corrinoids

High levels of this coenzyme have been recorded in four *Methanobrevibacter* species (1.3 to 1.8 nmol per mg protein) and in *Ms. barkeri* (3.2 to 8.2 nmol per mg protein) (Krzycki and Zeikus, 1980). Involvement of corrinoids in methanogenesis was suggested when crude extracts of both *Ms. barkeri* and *Mb. bryantii* (McBride and Wolfe, 1971) were shown to convert the methyl group of CH_3-B_{12} (a corrinoid protein) to methane, and the enzymatic transfer of methyl from CH_3-B_{12} to H-S-CoM has been demonstrated (Taylor and Wolfe, 1974). Shapiro (1982) presented evidence that corrinoids do not function in the conversion of methanol to methane and concluded that free corrinoids were not involved in methanogenesis, but that a protein-bound corrinoid was.

It has also been proposed by Keneally and Zeikus (1982) that corrinoids are involved in metabolic processes distinct from but related to methanogenesis. CH_3 - B_{12} is possibly part of a cell-carbon-regulating mechanism.

Methanopterin

The precise function of methanopterin is unknown, but it is clearly a carbon-carrying cofactor or prosthetic group, since it is labelled rapidly by $^{14}CO_2$. It is involved early in the carbon dioxide reduction steps and may be a component of the carbon dioxide reduction factor (CDR) required for carbon dioxide reduction to methyl-CoM. The CDR factor has been resolved into three components: CDR itself, a carbon dioxide binding non-pterin cofactor and a pterin-like formaldehyde-activating factor (FAF) which spectrally resembles methanopterin. FAF participates in two separated two-electron reductions and can carry carbon at the formyl, hydroxymethyl and methyl levels (Daniels *et al*, 1984).

54

Figure 7.1   Overview of the methanogenesis carbon pathway and its relation to cell carbon production

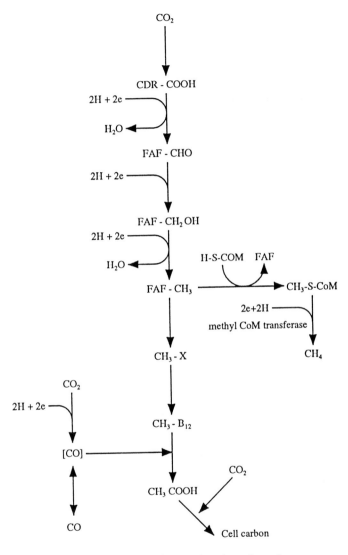

CDR   Carbon dioxide restriction factor (methanofuran)
FAF   Formaldehyde activating factor
CoM   Coenzyme M

Carbon dioxide reducing (CDR) factor (methanofuran)

The CDR factor is a carbon dioxide-binding cofactor essential for methanogenesis from carbon dioxide.

Enzymes

Hydrogenase

Hydrogenase normally splits hydrogen into protons and electrons. Nickel (Ni) has been shown to be a component of the enzyme but its role in catalysis or electron transfer is not understood.

Formate dehydrogenase

This enzyme has been demonstrated in crude extracts of three methanogens, *Mbr. smithii, Mb. formicicum* and *Mc. Vannielli*. The route of formate entry into the methanogenesis pathway is not known. It could be split to hydrogen and carbon dioxide and these substrates then converted to methane. Alternatively, formate could be oxidised by formate dehydrogenase and the electrons transferred to F_{420}, which would then reduce formate to methane.

Methyl-CoM reductase

The last step in the formation of methane is brought about by methyl-CoM reductase. The reaction requires ATP, magnesium (Mg), proteins (A_1, A_2, A_3), cofactors, and molecular hydrogen to provide the electrons. Coenzyme F_{420} appears to link the dehydrogenation of formate and the reduction of reduced nicotinamide adenine dinucleotide phosphate (NADPH) to oxidised nicotinamide adenine dinucleotide phosphate (NADP) with the hydrogenase reaction that supplies reducing power for the methyl reductase.

Methylene-FAF oxidoreductase

This enzyme is postulated to be involved in the methanogenic pathway, reducing formyl-FAF to methylene-FAF.

Electron transport

Ferredoxin F_{420} (5-Deazaflavin)

Ferredoxin F_{420} is found in all methane-producing bacteria and is widespread among the *Streptomyces*. It is structurally similar to a flavin, but its chemical properties make it more similar to nicotinamide, and it is chemically restricted to only two-electron transfers compared with flavins which carry out both one- and two-electron processes (Walsh, Jacobson and Ryerson, 1980).

The function of F_{420} is the transfer of electrons. It is reduced by hydrogen via hydrogenase and it can transfer electrons to NADP but not to nicotinamide adenine dinucleotide (NAD) using NADP-F_{420} oxidoreductase. F_{420} accepts two electrons from hydrogen and two hydrogen ions (H^+) from water (Daniels, Fulton, Spencer and Orme-Johnson, 1980), transferring the hydrogen atom at position 5 directly to the NADP. The direct electron donors for methanogenesis are unknown, but F_{420} is considered a likely candidate.

Nicotinamides

Methanogens have been found to contain nicotinamide in addition to the aforementioned F_{420}, which is of interest as both carry out similar two-electron transfer reactions. NADP can be reduced through NADP-F_{420} oxidoreductase; NAD, however, cannot be reduced via F_{420} nor directly from hydrogenase or formate dehydrogenase. The reduction pathway for NAD is not known. Since certain enzymes have an absolute requirement for reduced NAD (ie NADH) a reduction pathway must exist. A possible pathway is via glyceraldehyde-3-phosphate dehydrogenase, with the enzyme having a 10-fold greater affinity for reduced NADP (NADPH) in the reducing direction, while in the oxidising direction it has the same affinity for NAD or NADP. Since NADP can be reduced by F_{420} the concentration of NADP should be quite low while that of NAD should be higher, such that NADPH could reduce 3-phosphoglyceric acid to glyceraldehyde-3-phosphate. NAD could then be reduced to NADH. Experiments to verify this pathway have not been undertaken.

Carbon fixation into cell material

Methanogens not only derive energy from the production of methane but can also derive their cellular carbon from single carbon precursors. The methanogens have a modified reversed citric acid cycle, as shown in Figure 7.2. Production of acetate occurs via a $C_1 + C_1$ condensation of carbon atoms at different oxidation states (Stupperich, Hammel, Fuchs and Thauer, 1983). The biosynthesis by methanogens of all amino acids except isoleucine appears to be the same as in typical bacteria.

ATP synthesis

The preferred model for the physical arrangement of energy-producing proteins for carbon dioxide respiring methanogenesis is one with a proton pumping hydrogenase providing the electrochemical ion gradients required to perform essential functions, including ATP synthesis. Evidence for a Mitchellian transmembrane gradient is good, but there is merit in models that involve a proton layer or pool that is not in equilibrium with bulk phase water. ATP production is coupled to the methanogenic enzymes, which may be cytoplasmic but are most likely to be aggregated and membrane-associated. There are, however, many unsolved problems remaining for a complete understanding of the bio-energetics of the methanogens (Daniels *et al*, 1984).

Figure 7.2   Pathway of carbon dioxide assimilation by methanogenic bacteria

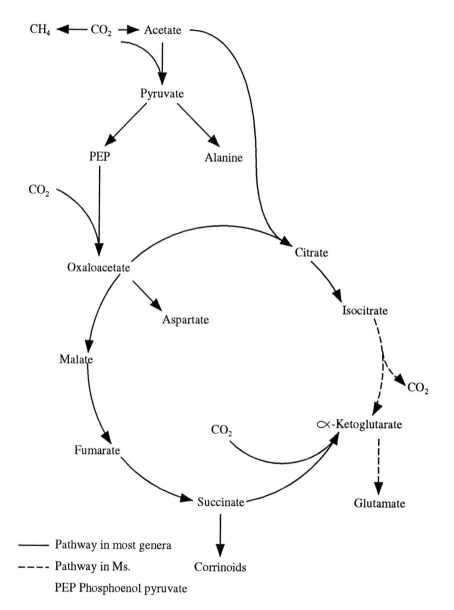

$CH_4 \longleftarrow CO_2 \longrightarrow$ Acetate

Pyruvate

PEP   Alanine

CO_2

Oxaloacetate   Citrate

Aspartate   Isocitrate

Malate CO_2

Fumarate CO_2 $\propto$-Ketoglutarate

Succinate   Glutamate

Corrinoids

——— Pathway in most genera

- - - - Pathway in Ms.

PEP Phosphoenol pyruvate

59

CHAPTER 8

METHANE PRODUCTION DURING DIGESTION

Substrates and pathways

As established earlier, none of the carbohydrate-fermenting bacteria and protozoa produce methane, but many of them produce formate, hydrogen and carbon dioxide as fermentation products. The hydrogen can be removed either through the formation of reduced fermentation products such as lactate ($CH_3CHOH\ COOH$) and ethanol (C_2H_5OH), or by the formation of hydrogen gas. In the mixed culture of the normal rumen, gaseous hydrogen is almost undetectable and methane is a large constituent of the gas phase. In addition the balance of the fermentation products lies towards acetate rather than the more reduced acids, and ethanol is not detectable.

It has been shown that hydrogen is a principal substrate for rumen methanogenesis by relating the rates of production of methane in rumen fluid to the dissolved hydrogen concentrations with various substrates added to a fermentation *in vitro* (Hungate, 1967). Formate produced by sugar-fermenting bacteria has been shown to be the substrate for about 18% of rumen methane formation (Hungate *et al*, 1970). Experiments using mixed rumen bacteria have also shown methane production to be proportional to hydrogen concentration when hydrogen was added to the gas phase (Czerkawski, Harfoot and Breckenridge, 1972).

The methanogenic bacteria maintain a low partial pressure of hydrogen within the rumen, due to their capacity to use hydrogen to reduce carbon dioxide to methane. The maintenance of this low partial pressure of hydrogen has a profound influence on the production of hydrogen and other products by the rest of the non-methanogenic rumen microbial population. This has been demonstrated by Moomaw and Hungate (1963), who studied the fermentation pathway of *Ruminococcus albus*.

R. albus ferments glucose by the Embden-Meyerhof-Parnas pathway to pyruvate ($CH_3COCOOH$) and NADH. Acetyl-coenzyme A (CoA), hydrogen and carbon dioxide are formed from pyruvate in a ferredoxin-dependent reaction. The catalytic amounts of NADH produced in the cell must be reoxidised, either by reduction of acetyl-CoA to acetaldehyde (CH_3COH) which in turn is reduced to ethanol by NADH, or by another ferredoxin-dependent system which produces hydrogen. The latter reaction only operates when hydrogen is removed, which is the case when cultures of *R. albus* are grown in the presence of methanogens. The former reaction is not affected by hydrogen concentration. The pathway of fermentation of glucose by *R. albus* is shown in Figure 8.1 (Glass, Bryant and Wolin, 1977).

Figure 8.1   **Pathway of fermentation of glucose by *Ruminococcus albus***

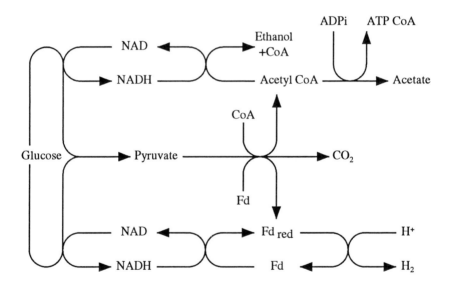

Fd = Ferredoxin

The effect of the maintenance of a low partial pressure of hydrogen by methanogens is to increase the total production of hydrogen and acetate by *R. albus*. This process is known as *interspecies hydrogen transfer*. It couples the oxidative reactions of the fermentation pathway of *R. albus* to the reductive reactions the methanogens use to reduce carbon dioxide to methane and it thereby eliminates the formation of ethanol. The added advantage of acetate production over the electron-sink fermentation product, ethanol, is that more ATP is produced for use by *R. albus* and the interspecies hydrogen transfer provides additional hydrogen for the methanogens, which gain increased energy by utilising it to produce more methane.

Interspecies hydrogen transfer has also been found to alter the fermentation pattern of other bacteria, such as *Ruminococcus flavefaciens* (Latham and Wolin, 1977) and *Selenomonas ruminantium* (Chen and Wolin, 1977). *S. ruminantium* has an important role in the production of VFAs, particularly propionate, in the rumen. It ferments carbohydrates (glucose and lactate) to lactate, propionate, acetate and carbon dioxide and produces only traces of hydrogen when it is grown by itself. The changes in fermentation products when *S. ruminantium* is cultured with *Methanobacterium ruminantium* are a significant decrease in propionate formation and an increase in acetate formation. It has been shown that hydrogen is produced by *S. ruminantium* when cultured alone, by oxidation of reduced pyridine nucleotides, and this is inhibited by its own increased hydrogen concentration. The oxidation of pyridine nucleotides necessary to sustain glycolysis results in the formation of mainly lactate or propionate as electron sink products, with glucose-grown or lactate-grown cells respectively. Co-culture with *M. ruminantium* removes hydrogen and permits the production of hydrogen from pyridine nucleotides to become a major electron sink. The pathways of the fermentation of glucose and lactate by *S. ruminantium* alone and in the presence of *M. ruminantium* are shown in Figures 8.2 and 8.3 respectively (Chen and Wolin, 1977).

The shift in the type of fermentation products as a result of interspecies hydrogen transfer probably plays a role in regulating the relative amounts of the VFAs formed in the rumen. An understanding of this could be important for increasing efficiency of fermentation, not only for the microorganisms but also for the host.

Hungate (1963) proposed a hypothesis that "Methane formation may be looked upon as an energy sink into which the hydrogen from all rumen organisms drain, allowing them a higher yield of ~P and generating additional ~P". This appears to be fully supported by the evidence of interspecies hydrogen transfer discussed. Apart from methanogenesis, hydrogen concentrations in the rumen may be kept low by organisms such as *Vibrio succinogenes*, which obtains energy for growth by coupling hydrogen oxidation to fumarate $(C_2H_2(COOH)_2)$ reduction which produces succinate $(C_2H_4(COOH)_2)$, an important intercellular propionate precursor (Jacobs and Wolin, 1963).

Figure 8.2   **Pathway for glucose fermentation by *S. ruminantium* in the absence and presence of** *M. ruminantium*

1. S. ruminantium

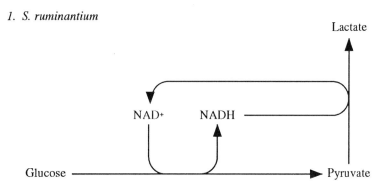

2. S. ruminantium + M. ruminantium

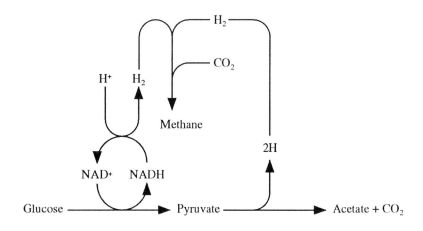

64

Figure 8.3   Pathway for lactate fermentation by *S. ruminantium* in the absence and presence of *M. ruminantium*

1. S. ruminantium

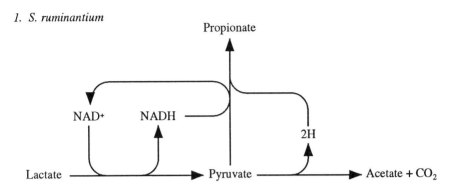

2. S. ruminantium + M. ruminantium

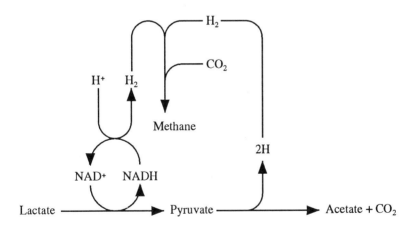

VFA production

A typical balance for the fermentation of carbohydrates in the rumen was calculated by Wolin (1960), as follows:

$$57.5 \text{ Hexose } (C_6H_{12}O_6) \rightarrow 65 \text{ acetate} + 20 \text{ propionate} + 15 \text{ butyrate} + 60 \ CO_2 + 35 \ CH_4 + 25 \ H_2O$$

In addition, small amounts of n-valerate ($CH_3(CH_2)_3COOH$) and n-caproate ($CH_3(CH_2)_4COOH$) are also sometimes produced. This balance may be divided into subsets of activities to show how a change in one subset will influence other subsets, and how the collective activities of different microbial populations influence the production of the major fermentation products (Wolin and Miller, 1988). The subset activities are:

$$\text{Hexose} \rightarrow 1.33 \text{ propionate} + 0.67 \text{ acetate} + 0.67 \text{ } CO_2 \quad (1)$$

$$\text{Hexose} \rightarrow \text{propionate} + \text{acetate} + H_2 + CO_2 \quad (1a)$$

$$\text{Hexose} \rightarrow \text{butyrate} + 2 H_2 + 2 CO_2 \quad (2)$$

$$\text{Hexose} \rightarrow 2 \text{ acetate} + 4 H_2 + 2 CO_2 \quad (3)$$

$$6 H_2 + 1.5 CO_2 \rightarrow 1.5 CH_4 + 3 H_2O \quad (4)$$

$$7 H_2 + 1.75 CO_2 \rightarrow 1.75 CH_4 + 3.5 H_2O \quad (4a)$$

sum of $(1)+(2)+(3)+(4)$

$$3 \text{ Hexose} \rightarrow 1.33 \text{ propionate} + 2.67 \text{ acetate} + \text{butyrate} + 1.5 CH_4 + 3.17 CO_2 + 3 H_2O \quad (5)$$

sum of $(1a)+(2)+(3)+(4a)$

$$3 \text{ Hexose} \rightarrow \text{propionate} + 3 \text{ acetate} + \text{butyrate} + 1.75 CH_4 + 3.25 CO_2 + 3.5 H_2O \quad (5a)$$

For simplicity, all substrates are considered to be composed of hexose units.

The above equations are based on a knowledge of the fermentations of individual rumen species, information about interactions between species and general information about bacterial fermentations. It should be noted that equation (3) is operative only if equation (4) or (4a) is operative, as equation (3) is dependent upon interspecies hydrogen transfer.

The relative rates of conversion of hexose into products by populations using equations (1), (2) and (3) and the activity of the rumen methanogens determine the course of the overall fermentation. If it is assumed that there is no selective absorption of VFAs from the rumen, then the relative rates determine the proportions of VFAs found in the rumen, and the ratios of methane formed to hexose used may be determined. Examples of the calculated ratios of methane formed to hexose used for various VFA concentrations are shown in Table 8.1 (Wolin and Miller, 1988).

Table 8.1   **Methane production and VFA concentrations in rumen contents**

Molar ratio acetate:propionate:butyrate	Moles methane produced per mole of hexose fermented[1]
65:20:15	0.61
60:25:15	0.54
55:30:15	0.48
70:20:10	0.64
65:25:10	0.57
60:30:10	0.50

[1] Calculated from equations (1), (1a), (2), (3) and (4)

Changes in the microbial populations responsible for the subset fermentations can influence the relative amounts of the major VFAs formed from dietary polysaccharides. This also has the effect of altering the proportion of methane produced.

When these equations are used to calculate methane production from feed intake, feed composition and VFA concentrations the values obtained invariably exceed those determined. For example, using VFA molar proportions and production rates on roughage diets (Leng, 1970), methane production rates between 8.39 and 11.92 kJ per 100 kJ feed energy were estimated, compared to a maximal production rate of 7.96 kJ, calculated from the regression equation proposed for roughage by Blaxter and Clapperton

(1965). The data indicated that, for roughage diets, hydrogen recovery varied between 78 and 96%. A possible reason for the discrepancies is the presence in the rumen of hydrogen acceptors not related to carbohydrate metabolism and of less quantitative importance, for example, nitrate ions (NO_3), sulphate ions and unsaturated fatty acids. Hydrogen donors not related to carbohydrates, such as the higher fatty acids, may also contribute hydrogen.

Demeyer and Van Nevel (1975) reported results from a series of experiments carried out to evaluate the stoichiometry described previously, by examining the effects of fermentation rate, diet and animal, and the effects of substrate on patterns of soluble carbohydrate fermentation. Differences were observed in the amounts of methane and VFAs produced and these were considered to be related to:

(a)   *Rate of fermentation* A single dose of substrate (glucose) compared with continuous infusion lowered methane production in favour of propionate production and also increased rumen fermentation rate.

(b)   *Animal* Rumen fluid from three sheep receiving the same diet showed differences in methane production which were related to differences in propionate production and rate of fermentation when cellobiose plus maltose was the substrate.

(c)   *Diet* A diet of hay and molasses gave a higher butyrate production compared to a diet of hay and concentrates. This pattern of VFAs, normally attributed to protozoal activity, is related to bacterial activity with molasses-fed animals (Hobson, 1972). Infusion of sucrose into the rumen resulted in a shift from methane and butyrate production to propionate production.

(d)   *Substrate* Substrates studied were galactose, xylose, sucrose, cellobiose, glucose, arabinose and rhamnose. Galactose and rhamnose had the lowest and highest levels of propionate production respectively, and also the highest and lowest levels of methane production respectively. These results illustrated the relationship between methane and propionate production.

The observation that a single large dose of soluble carbohydrates increases fermentation rate, increases propionate production and lowers methane production agrees with the decreased acetate:propionate ratio observed in animals fed diets rich in starch *ad libitum* (Ørskov, Flatt and Moe, 1968). The increase in fermentation rate alone may be responsible for the shift from methane production to the more rapid propionate production, occurring in a single cell. However, a decreased rumen pH has been observed with diets rich in starch fed *ad libitum* (Eadie, Hyldgaard-Jensen, Mann, Reid and Whitelaw, 1970) and this, coupled to high fermentation rates and propionate proportions, may inhibit methanogenic bacteria and rumen ciliates (Demeyer and Henderickx, 1967a; Eadie *et al*, 1970; respectively).

It has been shown that when a barley diet is fed to cattle in amounts below appetite, development of a large ciliate population occurs which results in an increase in the proportion of butyrate to propionate in the rumen liquor. Rumen pH, VFA concentrations and an increased methane production differ from changes encountered on intakes *ad libitum* (Eadie *et al*, 1970). Methanogens have been observed to associate closely with the rumen ciliates (Stumm, Gijzen and Vogels, 1982). Although metabolic interactions have not been demonstrated, Krumholz, Forsberg and Veira (1983) proposed that the close physical association between rumen entodiniomorphid ciliates and methanogenic bacteria enhanced interspecies hydrogen transfer. The rumen holotrich protozoa have a unique organelle, the hydrogenosome, which enables consumption of oxygen and production of hydrogen (Williams, 1986). Hillman, Lloyd and Williams (1988) showed that a metabolic interaction (ie interspecies hydrogen transfer) between methanogens and holotrich ciliate protozoa may occur in the rumen despite the sensitivity of methanogens to oxygen.

Protozoa can thus have significant effects on digestibility, methane production and metabolisability of energy, dependent on the diet. Whitelaw, Eadie, Bruce and Shand (1984) found a lower methane production in defaunated animals when only concentrates were offered, and the opposite was true from a hay-only ration (Itabashi, Kobayashi and Matsumoto, 1984). Kreuzer, Kirchgessner and Muller (1986) showed that defaunation reduced methane formation on a high cellulose diet and on a high starch diet containing steam-flaked maize, but had no effect on methane formation when the starch was from native maize. A possible explanation for the reduced methane production is an alteration in rumen fermentation pattern after defaunation. Defaunation leads to an increased propionate content at the expense of butyrate content (Whitelaw *et al*, 1984) which, as mentioned earlier, has an inverse relationship with methane formation. These shifts in fermentation pattern arise from the fact that most protozoa degrade carbohydrates mainly to butyric and acetic acids and less to propionic acid (Itabashi *et al*, 1984).

Moe and Tyrrell (1979) demonstrated relationships between diet composition, intake and methane production *in vivo* using dairy cows. They showed that over a range of intakes (2.7 to 22.93 kg dry matter/day) the production of methane per gram of cellulose digested was nearly three times that per gram of hemicellulose digested and five times that per gram of soluble fraction digested. It was suggested that the differences were due to a substantially lower proportion of the soluble fractions being fermented in the rumen and a larger proportion being digested and absorbed as glucose in the small intestine. When 26 soluble carbohydrates were studied in an artificial rumen it was found that, with the exception of rhamnose, the amount of methane produced was not dependent on the type of carbohydrate, but rather the amount of carbohydrate fermented (Czerkawski and Breckenridge, 1969). Experiments *in vivo* showed that the production of methane was influenced by the nature of the carbohydrate digested, but that this effect was relatively less important at low, rather than at high feed intakes (Moe and Tyrrell, 1979).

Researchers have also suggested that glucose and other simple sugars would give little methane, that cellulose was a good source of methane and that foods rich in either of the two types of carbohydrate would give corresponding amounts of methane (Czerkawski, 1969). This was found not to be the case when sheep were fed a dried grass ration containing 25 to 30% cellulose and 10% simple sugars; the production of 30 litres of methane per day was recorded, compared to 45 litres of methane per day when a molassed sugar beet pulp ration containing 15% cellulose and 25 to 30% simple sugars was fed. This result was unexpected and confirmed that in the situation described the estimations of methane produced from different dietary components were not additive.

Blaxter and Wainman (1964) measured methane production from sheep and steers fed various proportions of hay and maize at two planes of nutrition. Methane production was shown to increase with increasing proportions of roughage and the divergence between the values for different levels of nutrition increased with the proportion of maize. Also, the observed methane production of the mixed rations was higher and deviated considerably from the hypothetical additive values. The extent of the deviation appeared to be greater at maintenance than at two times maintenance. There are two possibilities to explain the non-additivity:

1.   The presence of the concentrate (maize) increased methane production from the less readily available carbohydrate of the

roughage.

2.   The presence of the less readily available carbohydrate (fibre) increased the methanogenic potential of the concentrate.

Which of these explanations, if either, is correct is yet to be determined. It has been recorded that when cereal diets are fed in combination with long hay a larger proportion of starch escapes rumen fermentation (Thomson and Lamming, 1972). These authors postulated that this was because the presence of large particles in the rumen increases the rate of passage of the smaller particles. More starch escaping rumen fermentation would allow more stable rumen conditions, especially in terms of pH, and would allow the rumen fermentation pattern to remain more in favour of acetate production compared with propionate production, which would give rise to increased levels of methane. Measurement of rumen VFA patterns in the earlier mentioned experiments may have helped to confirm the reason for the recorded data.

The lower levels of methane produced from the mixed rations at a feeding level two times maintenance compared to maintenance (Blaxter and Wainman, 1964) was also noted by Blaxter and Clapperton (1965) over a whole range of diets. It was found that as the amount of feed given was increased absolute methane production increased, although methane production per unit of feed consumed fell with increasing feed level. Methane production at a maintenance feeding level increased with increasing apparent digestibility of dietary energy, although this relationship was less clear at two times maintenance, and at three times maintenance it was thought that a negative relationship would occur. Level of feeding had little effect on methane production with low quality feeds (40 to 50% digestibility of dietary energy).

The loss of digestible energy from ruminant feeds in the form of methane gas has often been assumed to be about 8% of the gross energy intake. This is a substantial loss. The use of the metabolisable energy (ME) system to describe the energy value of ruminant diets depends on either direct measurement of methane production or an adequate means of estimating it. As methane production is a gaseous loss, its measurement requires specialised equipment. Therefore the ME content of many feedstuffs is estimated using a predicted value for methane energy loss. Attempts have been made by many workers to predict the extent of methane production in terms of easily measured parameters such as dry matter intake (Kriss, 1930), the amount of apparently digested carbohydrate (Swift, Bratzler, James, Tillman and Meek, 1948) and

71

the amount of apparently digested dietary gross energy (Blaxter and Clapperton, 1965). None of these relationships has proved satisfactory, probably because the amounts of methane produced by animals are affected by many factors, particularly the type and quantity of the diet.

The digestion of protein in the rumen has also been shown to give rise to methane production (Blaxter and Martin, 1962). An infusion of casein into the rumen of sheep gave an increase in methane production of 7.6 kcal per 100 kcal casein (3.3 g methane per 100 g casein). This may indicate that when nitrogen is limiting in the rumen methane production is limited. The major source of cell nitrogen to methanogenic bacteria is ammonia. It has been noted (Schwartz and Gilchrist, 1975) that in general an increase in the proportion of readily fermentable carbohydrates in the ration increases the uptake of nitrogen by the microorganisms in the rumen. This is the result of increased availability of energy for growth and a reduction in the energy needed for maintenance by fast growing organisms. More nitrogen is incorporated when the fermentation yields a high proportion of propionate than when there is a high proportion of acetate or butyrate. This increase in nitrogen utilisation means that the diet must supply more rumen degradable nitrogen if nitrogen is not to become limiting for bacterial growth. When nitrogen is limiting the species most likely to suffer are those which grow more slowly, such as the cellulolytic bacteria and the methane producers (Schwartz and Gilchrist, 1975).

CHAPTER 9

CONTROL OF METHANOGENESIS

Methanogenesis results in a loss of food energy and a loss of carbon to the rumen and means of reducing these losses have been intensively investigated (Czerkawski, 1969). If methane production is decreased, an increased production of propionate should theoretically occur, resulting in an increase in the efficiency of feed energy use. The converse should also apply, that is if the production of propionate is increased, methane production should decrease, again improving energetic efficiency.

Intensive research efforts have been directed towards the discovery of chemical agents which will modulate ruminal fermentation to improve feed efficiency. Before reviewing this research it is worth noting that overall the complex ecological system of the rumen works efficiently, particularly with respect to cellulolysis. Therefore any attempt to modify methane production should be selective and cause minimum disturbance to the rest of the rumen fermentation.

The most natural way to depress methane production would be to manipulate the diet to give high rates of fermentation and/or passage through the rumen, which might increase the molar percentage of propionate and decrease that of acetate in the rumen VFAs. Such changes in VFA proportions have been associated with a decrease in the fibre content of the ration, or in the particle size of the feed, or with an increase in the level and frequency of feeding (Thomas and Clapperton, 1972). These conditions increase the ME content of the feed and also the efficiency of utilisation of ME for fattening (Flatt, Moe, Moore, Hooven, Lehman, Ørskov and Hemken, 1969).

The latter increase has been related previously to the poorer utilisation of acetate compared with propionate. Experiments in which the pure acids were infused singly into the rumens of fasting sheep showed a difference in efficiency, which was 0.59 for acetate and 0.86 for propionate (Armstrong and Blaxter, 1957). Later experiments with lambs which were entirely sustained on infusions of mixtures of VFAs into the rumen and casein into the abomasum (Ørskov, Grub, Smith, Webster and Corrigall, 1979) seemed to disprove this theory. When the VFA infusion mixture was changed from one having a molar composition of acetate:propionate:butyrate of 75:15:10 to one of 45:35:20 respectively the efficiency of utilisation of ME was unchanged.

The latter results can be explained if the efficient utilisation of acetate is dependent on its conversion into fatty acids and then into triglycerides (MacRae and Lobley, 1982). These metabolic steps require both reducing equivalents (NADPH) and glycerol phosphate. Where provision of the precursors of these co-factors was adequate, that is mainly from propionate in animals given mixed diets, or from glucogenic amino acids in the "infusion animals" which were receiving 23% of their ME intake as casein, the conversion of acetate into fatty acids could proceed and the efficiency of utilisation of ME was high. In conditions where the level of these two glycolytic intermediates is low (ie poor quality forage diets), the animal may have a problem in clearing the absorbed acetate and may need to catabolise the acetate through oxidative substrate cycles, which give increased heat production and hence a lower efficiency of utilisation of ME.

The work discussed above shows that the manipulation of diet to alter the VFA profile in favour of propionate in turn depresses methane production. However, the overall effects of this on the efficiency of utilisation of ME are not as straightforward as once thought, and the complexity goes beyond the consideration of VFAs in isolation.

Attention has been given more recently to the use of chemical additives directed specifically at inhibiting methane production. Information available to date suggests that lower methane production must be accompanied either by an increased synthesis of more reduced end-products of rumen fermentation, such as propionate or butyrate, or by the evolution of hydrogen. The compounds considered as inhibitors of methanogenesis can therefore be split into two major groups. One group comprises those compounds that are able to divert hydrogen from methanogenesis by competitive inhibition, for example higher unsaturated fatty acids (Czerkawski, Blaxter and Wainman, 1966a), sulphate and nitrate. Compounds in the other group have a specific toxic effect on the methanogenic bacteria.

A comprehensive review of the literature on the chemical control of rumen microbial metabolism was carried out by Chalupa (1980). The following section therefore updates the main findings in this review and evaluates the current situation.

Ionophores

Ionophores are molecules with "backbones" of various structures that contain strategically spaced oxygen atoms. The backbone is capable of assuming conformations that focus these oxygen atoms about a ring or cavity into which a cation may fit. Hence their biological activity is related to their ability to modulate the movement of cations such as sodium (Na), potassium (K) and calcium (Ca) across cell membranes (Pressman, 1976).

Some ionophores have been reported to cause an increase in propionate production, for example monensin, lasalocid, salinomycin, nigercin and gramicidin. These are all, with the exception of gramicidin, carboxylic ionophores, whilst gramicidin is a channel-forming ionophore. Valinomycin is a neutral ionophore and does not enhance propionate production by a mixed rumen microbial population.

Monensin

This compound is known to adjust several pathways of fermentation. In a mixed rumen microbial population it consistently increases the production of propionate, decreases acetate and butyrate production, and partially inhibits methanogenesis, with no accumulation of hydrogen. Monensin has also been shown to decrease the degradation of an exogenous amino acid load and to lower rumen ammonia levels. Studies *in vivo* on animal performance have shown Rumensin (commercial product with monensin sodium as the active ingredient) supplementation to improve feed efficiency, either by reducing feed intake and maintaining weight gain or *vice versa* (Chalupa, 1977). Raun, Cooley, Potter, Rathmacher and Richardson, (1976) reported that increased ruminal energetic efficiency produced by Rumensin did not account for all the feed efficiency improvements obtained in cattle. It was suggested that the improvements in the efficiency of growth were not solely due to ruminal energy conservation but also to decreased ruminal losses of amino nitrogen caused by suppression of deamination and perhaps proteolysis. In fact, there were greater responses with Rumensin in diets containing marginal versus adequate levels of protein, which further implicates fermentative adjustments involving amino nitrogen.

Martin and Macy (1985) showed that 10 mg of monensin per kg rumen fluid added to a mixed rumen culture *in vitro* reduced methane production by 16%,

75

with no accumulation of hydrogen, whilst Russell and Martin (1984) used 2 mg of monensin per kg rumen fluid in a mixed rumen bacteria incubation *in vitro* and recorded a 51% inhibition of methane production. The difference in the effectiveness of monensin described could be due to differences in the substrates used for microbial growth.

Dietary factors, including energy and protein level, the presence of buffers and mineral concentrations, affect the response to ionophores. The relative affinity of ionophores for specific ions is likely to be a factor in the mechanism of the response (Bergen and Bates, 1984). It is thought that the decreased methane production is a result of selection against gram-positive hydrogen-producing bacteria (eg *Ruminococcus albus*), which in turn deprives the methane bacteria of one essential growth requirement (Bergen and Bates, 1984). The increased propionate production results from selection for succinate-forming bacteria (eg *Bacteroides succinogenes*) and for propionate producers that decarboxylate succinate to propionate (eg *Selenomonas ruminantium*). From results obtained *in vitro* with additions of sodium, potassium and ionophores, Romatowski (1979) suggested that it is the entry of sodium ions into microbial cells which is directly responsible for the effects of ionophores on VFA production. It was hence proposed that monensin selects for rumen microbes which are more tolerant to sodium.

Research *in vivo* on the effects of monensin on digestibility, methanogenesis and the heat increment of a maize based concentrate: silage mixture fed to steers was undertaken by Wedegaertner and Johnson (1983). Monensin at a rate of 3 mg per $kg^{0.75}$ body weight improved the apparent digestibilities of energy, neutral detergent fibre and crude protein, and methane production was reduced by 26%. Dietary ME was increased, resulting in an increase in retained energy. Both net energy for maintenance (NE_m) and net energy for growth (NE_g) were improved by approximately 7% by monensin. Approximately one-third of the improved energy utilisation was explained by the reduced methanogenesis caused by monensin and two- thirds by reduced faecal losses. In contrast, Byers (1980) indicated that monensin decreased maintenance requirements and/or increased the efficiency of dietary energy use for maintenance while not altering the net efficiency of energy use for growth, when steers were fed maize silage diets.

The above work indicates an impact on metabolic function and efficiency. Pond (1985) suggested that one mode of action of antibiotics and ionophores that have antibiotic effects is *via* a reduction in the size of the liver, thus

76

reducing maintenance requirements. A systemic mode of action is therefore possible in addition to the intraruminal responses observed. Benz, Byers, Schelling, Greene, Lunt and Smith (1989) studied this theory for monensin given to steers at a rate of 33 mg per kg feed for 46 days prior to slaughter. Liver weight was unaffected, but changes in the levels of intermediary metabolites of carbohydrate metabolism suggested alterations in hepatic carbohydrate metabolism favouring gluconeogenesis in steers fed monensin, which is consistent with an increase in propionate production in the rumen.

Bogaert, Jouany and Jeminet (1990) studied the incidence of a chemical structure modification of monensin on its activity *in vitro*. Monensin-propionate was derived from monensin by acylation of the -CH_2 OH radical at the end of the monensin molecule, on the C_{26} giving a -CH_2-O-$COCH_2CH_3$ group. This appeared to amplify slightly the action of this molecule on fermentations. Monensin decreased methane production by 33% whereas monensin-propionate decreased it by 38%.

A 28-week cattle growth trial with monensin showed a 21% reduction in methane production which was maintained throughout the trial (Davies, Nwaonu, Stanier and Boyle, 1982). This suggests that there is little or no adaptation to monensin.

Other ionophores

Ionophores other than monensin have been less well documented. Lasalocid has produced fermentative adjustments like those of monensin and improvements in animal performance were similar in cattle supplemented with lasalocid or monensin (Chalupa, 1980). Lasalocid (2 mg per kg rumen fluid) inhibited methane production by 44% and decreased ammonia production, with mixed rumen bacteria that were incubated with an excess of protein hydrolysate (Russell and Martin, 1984).

Calcimycin was discovered in 1972 (Reed and Lardy, 1972). However, there has been little study of its action on rumen fermentation. Caffarel-Mendez, Demuynck and Jeminet (1986) observed during a short-term (6 hours) fermentation *in vitro* that calcimycin, unlike monensin, increased butyrate production at the expense of propionate, though this result was not repeated in more recent work by Bogaert *et al* (1990). In fact, the latter researchers observed an absence of effects on the pattern of rumen fermentation and on ammonia production, and no reduction in methanogenesis.

Similar results were found with abierixin, another ionophore more recently discovered by David, Leal Ayala and Tabet (1985). The low activity of abierixin on fermentation patterns is not surprising due to its weak antibiotic properties (David et al, 1985), when compared with those of monensin (Gaboyard, 1987). In contrast, the total lack of effect of calcimycin in no way reflects its potent antibiotic action (Liu, 1982).

Bogaert et al (1990) noted that the aptitude of the aforementioned compounds to reduce the acetate to propionate ratio coincided with their aptitude to transport the potassium ion effectively. In fact, monensin possesses very marked ionophore properties for potassium ions, even though it is better known for its ability to carry sodium ions (Gaboyard, 1987). Calcimycin is a good carrier of calcium and magnesium ions and is less able to carry potassium ions, like abierixin which has low ionophore properties.

Some of the ionophores (eg monensin and lasalocid) have been shown partially to inhibit methanogenesis in the rumen, with the added advantages that they enhance energy efficiency and limit ruminal protein degradation.

Halogenated compounds

Halogen-containing chemicals are potent inhibitors of methanogenesis. The degree of activity has usually been related to the number and type of halogens on the molecule. Iodine- based compounds are more effective than bromine-based compounds, which in turn are more effective than chlorine-based compounds (Prins, 1978). Consequently a large number of halogenated chemicals, such as polyhalogenated alcohols, aldehydes, acids, esters, and hemiacetyls of sugars and starch, have been tested for antimethanogenic activity.

The hemiacetal of chloral hydrate and starch increased the production in vitro of propionate and butyrate at the expense of acetate production; methane production was suppressed by 70%, although hydrogen gas was shown to accumulate. This indicates that the mechanism of action of halogenated compounds is a selective toxic effect upon methanogenic bacteria, and that they irreversibly react with reduced vitamin B_{12} to inhibit cobamide-dependent methanogenesis. However, vitamin B_{12} derivatives do not now appear to be cofactors in methanogenesis (Prins, 1978).

Observed adjustments to rumen fermentation *in vivo* have been similar to those described for experiments *in vitro* (Chalupa, 1977). Gas losses decreased overall, so that energy retention increased, but the efficiency of utilisation of the additional ME for maintenance plus production was unchanged. Data on the effects of halogen-containing chemicals upon animal performance are inconclusive. There seems to be a consistent reduction in feed intake with little, no or a negative change in weight gain. Some studies with cattle have shown large decreases in feed intake and live weight gain. Possible explanations include dysfunctions caused by hydrogen or hydrogen acceptors, impaired ruminal production of vitamin B_{12}, ineffective metabolism of additional propionate and taste aversions to or subclinical toxicities of halogen-containing chemicals (Chalupa, 1977).

Rumen microbes *in vivo* have adapted to both amichloral and trichloroethyl adipate after about four weeks (Clapperton, 1977). Chloroform appeared to be the only known halogen-containing chemical which was a persistent antimethanogen, but it is very volatile and not practical as a feed additive.

Experiments on the polyhalogenated compound 2, 4-bis (trichloromethyl)-benzo [1, 3] dioxin-6-carboxylic acid (ICI 13409) showed a large inhibition of methanogenesis with a concomitant stimulation of hydrogen production. Ruminal propionate production increased and that of acetate decreased (Davies *et al*, 1982). In a 28-week growth trial in beef cattle, inclusion of ICI 13409 in the concentrate element of the diet, at a level of 6 mg per kg bodyweight, improved liveweight gain by 8% and reduced feed intake by 5% with respect to the control. Conversion of dietary energy into energy retained in the animal was also improved. There was a marked reduction in methane production (65%) and this was maintained, with a slight upward trend towards the end of the experiment.

Bromoethanesulphonic acid has been shown to reduce methane accumulation by 76% (Martin and Macy, 1985), and to increase hydrogen production. Bromoethanesulphonic acid significantly decreased the acetate:propionate ratio when incubated with either hay or soluble carbohydrates but not with a mixed diet. Gunsalus, Romesser and Wolfe (1978) showed that bromoethanesulphonic acid inhibits the methyl coenzyme M reductase of methanogens and hence hydrogen and carbon dioxide are not utilised.

Chloral hydrate has been shown to be a potent inhibitor of rumen methane production and directly toxic to methanogenic bacteria. In rumen fluid chloral hydrate is partially converted to chloroform, which is considered to be the active agent and which may inhibit methanogenesis by blocking methyl transfer to coenzyme M. In the presence of chloral hydrate, methane production was decreased by 96%, and propionate production increased at the expense of acetate (Mathers and Miller, 1982). Sheep receiving 1.5 g per day of chloral hydrate died from liver damage after about 250 days (Lanigan, Payne and Peterson, 1978). There have been no reports of hepatotoxicity with chloroform, chloral hydrate or hemiacetal of chloral and starch administration for up to 98 days in sheep (Clapperton, 1974) or 112 days in cattle (Horton, 1980). This work showed that long term animal studies are required, not only to establish the persistence of the methane inhibition, but to ensure that the product is not toxic to the animal.

Other chemicals

Unsaturated fatty acids

The use of higher unsaturated fatty acids as potential competitive inhibitors has shown considerable inhibition of methanogenesis, not entirely accounted for by hydrogenation of the limited amounts used (Czerkawski, Blaxter and Wainman, 1966a). This finding was also associated with an increase in propionate production both *in vitro* and *in vivo* (Demeyer and Henderickx, 1967b; Czerkawski, 1973 respectively). Although inhibitory activity increases with the degree of unsaturation of acids, a non-competitive mechanism is clearly involved since palmitic acid, which is saturated, will also reduce methane production (Czerkawski *et al*, 1966a). Inhibitory activity is maximal with non-conjugated cis configuration of the double bonds and a free, preferentially unionised, carboxyl group is necessary (Demeyer and Henderickx, 1967b). This suggests a physico-chemical mechanism of inhibition involving adhesion of the fatty acids to the cells, possibly uncoupling energy systems and related to the presence of a large non-polar group. This may explain why saturated fatty acids also inhibit methanogenesis.

Higher fatty acids depressed butyrate production, which was probably related to an inhibitory effect on protozoa (Czerkawski, 1973). Pure strains of propionate producing bacteria were unaffected. Diets with high levels of easily fermented carbohydrates prevented rumen lipolysis and made the use of triglycerides ineffective for inhibition of methane, as this requires the presence of free fatty acids (Nicholson and Sutton, 1971).

Czerkawski, Blaxter and Wainman, (1966b) reported that linolenic acid reduced methane production by 75% but was also associated with a reduction in cellulose digestion. Lipid digestibility increased as a result of the proportion of bacterial fatty acids decreasing. Hence the ME available increased, but the efficiency of ME utilisation was unaltered. Rapid infusion of linolenic acid resulted in a greater reduction of methane production compared with continuous infusion, when sheep were fed high quality diets.

Sulphite

Sulphite ions (SO_3) were initially considered to be competitive inhibitors of methanogenesis and were found to increase propionate and decrease methane production. However, sulphite incorporated into the diet did not improve animal performance for fattening (Demeyer and Van Nevel, 1975).

Combinations of chemical agents

Treatment of batch cultures with monensin or amicloral has produced the previously described shifts in fermentation. Monensin plus amicloral produced fermentative adjustments comparable to those predicted from cultures treated with monensin and amicloral alone (Chalupa, Corbett and Brethour, 1978). In steers fed sorghum silage based diets, Rumensin and amicloral had a complementary affect upon feed efficiency (Brethour and Chalupa, 1977). This was not found to be the case with mixed diets (Horton, Bassendowski and Keeler, 1979). The additivity of these adjustments to fermentation is a reflection of the two chemical agents manipulating ruminal reactions by different mechanisms.

The continuous culture technique has been used to test the effect of the combination of monensin and isoacids (equal proportions of isobutyric, 2-methyl-butyric, isovaleric and valeric acids) on fermentation patterns. Isoacids alone increased acetate and total VFA production, with no effect on methane production. Monensin alone reduced acetate and total VFA production but increased that of propionate. Methane production was reduced by 26%. The combination of isoacids and monensin increased acetate concentration relative to monensin alone, but did not alter the effect of monensin on propionate concentration (Kone, Machado and Cook, 1989). Effects on methanogenesis were not reported.

81

Consequences of chemical control

All of the chemicals discussed show the complexity of effects to be considered when using them to inhibit methanogenesis. For example, cellulolysis and fermentation rate may be depressed, protozoa may be inhibited, in some cases proteolysis is depressed and hydrogen can accumulate. These effects may decrease microbial growth and alter the extent and site of protein and energy digestion. Feed intake may also be affected. The relative importance of these factors is dependent on diet type. The level of propionate is invariably increased, but the overall effect on animal performance may be debatable and requires much thought. Inhibition of methanogenesis is relatively simple to achieve, but the accompanying effects may prevent a beneficial result of such inhibition for the animal.

Another problem associated with controlling rumen metabolism with chemical agents is the potential risk of an agent or its metabolites accumulating in the animal products or excreta and subsequently being harmful to man and the environment. This makes the use of naturally occurring substances, such as fatty acids, or simply manipulation of the diet much better propositions.

Armstrong and Gilbert (1985) suggested the potential use of recombinant deoxyribonucleic acid (DNA) technology to modify the fermentation characteristics of rumen microorganisms. Examples of application include an enhanced celluloytic activity in the rumen biomass for forage fed animals to increase their supply of VFAs and amino acids; and a reduction in methanogenesis accompanied by an alternative hydrogen sink through increasing propionate production. This approach may appear simple but again it may have many unforeseen problems.

PART 3

CONCLUSIONS

CHAPTER 10

CONCLUSIONS

This book briefly summarises the major sources of greenhouse gases and their potential impact on global warming, with particular emphasis on methane. Carbon dioxide is the most abundant trace gas, being added to the atmosphere in the greatest quantity, and it is expected to cause about 50% of the global warming in the next half century. Methane is generally considered to be the second most important greenhouse gas and is expected to contribute 18% of future warming. Methane's strong ability to absorb infra-red radiation, combined with its relatively short atmospheric lifetime makes its control an important opportunity for addressing global climate change.

The current literature suggests, with little doubt, that the gases deemed to have a greenhouse effect are increasing in terms of tropospheric concentration. The evidence of the effect of these changing concentrations on climatic change (global warming) is far from clear and existing climate models still have major uncertainties.

The rate of increase in atmospheric methane concentration in recent years has been approximately 1% per year. The sources contributing to these increasing levels are currently under debate, but the major producers of atmospheric methane are natural wetlands, rice paddies and enteric fermentation, contributing approximately 20%, 20% and 15% respectively to the total methane flux. Biomass burning, natural gas, coal mining, landfill sites and methane hydrates all contribute to the total methane flux to a lesser extent. In all cases, however, the estimates are subject to large variation and require improved methods of prediction. The total methane flux is currently estimated to be equal to 540 (± 100) x 10^9 kg per year. About 30% of the total flux is produced from naturally occurring sources while the remaining 70% of emissions are from anthropogenic sources.

It was established in Part 1 that the world ruminant population produces between 70 and 100 Tg methane per year, equivalent to approximately 15 to 20% of the total methane flux. Of this, 75% is generated by the domestic cattle population, mainly in the developed world. Methane is one of the end products of rumen microbial fermentation and the methanogenic bacteria are reliant upon other bacteria for the supply of their substrates (carbon dioxide, hydrogen and formate). This dependency is only a part of a very complex system which, despite extensive research into rumen microbiology, is still not completely understood.

Methane production by ruminants is difficult to measure and requires expensive, specialised equipment. The complex nature of the rumen microbial fermentation also makes the level of methane production difficult to predict. To date there has been insufficient research on the effects of diet type and interactions within mixed diets on the quantity of methane produced. Level of feeding has been shown to have an effect on methane production, particularly with high quality feeds. The effect of this with diet type and mixed diets still merits further research.

Much research has been carried out on the manipulation of rumen fermentation to inhibit methanogenesis, with a view to increasing energetic efficiency. Use of naturally occurring dietary components, for example long chain fatty acids, has been shown to inhibit methanogenesis in some situations, but no improvement in energetic efficiency has been noted. Many chemical inhibitors, for example ionophores and halogenated compounds, have been investigated and have proved to be effective in decreasing methane production to varying degrees. Problems with these chemicals have been noted, such as rumen microbial adaptation, toxicity to the host, volatility preventing successful incorporation into diets and an inability to increase energetic efficiency.

Current worldwide research efforts include better estimation of methane emissions from ruminants; studies on the supplementation of poor quality forages to increase the productivity of ruminants and reduce methane emissions; development of models to determine methane emissions from ruminant animals; and development of instrumentation to measure methane from ruminants in the field. Possibilities for reducing methane production from ruminants which require more research include the development of persistent ionophores and compounds to inhibit protozoa, and the enhancement of acetogens (which will produce acetate from hydrogen and carbon dioxide as opposed to methane) in the rumen.

The uncertainties surrounding the emission factors for all sources of methane make development of an optimal greenhouse gas reduction strategy difficult. Research is needed to refine estimates of emissions for each of the sources and to develop technologies and management practices to reduce emissions.

BIBLIOGRAPHY

Alperin, M J and Reeburgh, W S (1984) Geochemical observations supporting anaerobic methane oxidation. In: *Microbial Growth on C-1 Compounds* (Editors R L Crawford and R S Hanson). American Society of Microbiology, Washington DC, 282-289.

Anderson, K L, Tayne, T A and Ward, D M (1987) Formation and fate of fermentation products in hot spring cyanobacterial mats. *Applied Environment Microbiology*, **53**, 2343-2352.

Annison, E F and Lewis D (1959) *Metabolism in the Rumen*. Methuen, London.

Armstrong, D G and Blaxter, K L (1957) The heat increment of steam-volatile fatty acids in fasting sheep. *British Journal of Nutrition*, **11**, 247-270.

Armstrong, D G and Gilbert, H J (1985) Biotechnology and the rumen. *Journal of the Science of Food and Agriculture*, **36**, 655-656.

Arrhenius, S (1896) On the influence of carbonic acid in the air upon the temperature of the ground. *Philosophical Magazine*, **41**, 237.

Aselmann, I and Crutzen, P J (1989) Freshwater wetlands: Global distribution of natural wetlands and rice paddies, their net primary productivity, seasonality and possible methane emissions. *Journal of Atmospheric Chemistry*, **8**, 307-358.

Balch, W E and Wolfe, R S (1979) Specificity and biological distribution of coenzyme M (2-mercaptosulphonic acid). *Journal of Bacteriology*, **137**, 256-263.

Balch, W E, Fox, G E, Magrum, L J, Woese, C R and Wolfe, R S (1979) Methanogens: Reevaluation of a unique biological group. *Microbiological Reviews*, **43**, 260-296.

Bauchop, T (1979) Rumen anaerobic fungi of cattle and sheep. *Applied and Environmental Microbiology*, **38**, 148-158.

Beijer, W H (1952) Methane formation in the rumen of cattle. *Nature*, **170**, 576-577.

Benz, D A, Byers, F M, Schelling, G T, Greene, L W, Lunt, D K and Smith, S B (1989) Ionophores alter hepatic concentrations of intermediary carbohydrate metabolites in steers. *Journal of Animal Science*, **67**, 2393-2399.

Bergen, W G and Bates, D B (1984) Ionophores: Their effect on production efficiency and mode of action. *Journal of Animal Science*, **58**, 1465-1483.

Bingemer, H G and Crutzen, P J (1987) The production of methane from solid wastes. *Journal of Geophysical Research*, **92**, 2181-2187.

Blake, D R (1984) *Increasing Concentrations of Atmospheric Methane, 1979-1980.* PhD Thesis, University of California, Irvine, USA.

Blaxter, K L and Martin, A K (1962) The utilisation of protein as a source of energy in fattening sheep. *British Journal of Nutrition*, **16**, 397-407.

Blaxter, K L and Wainman, F W (1964) The utilization of the energy of different rations by sheep and cattle for maintenance and for fattening. *Journal of Agricultural Science*, **63**, 113-128.

Blaxter, K L and Clapperton, J L (1965) Prediction of the amount of methane produced by ruminants. *British Journal of Nutrition*, **19**, 511-522.

Blaxter, K L and Czerkawski, J (1966) Modifications on the methane production of the sheep by supplementation of its diet. *Journal of the Science of Food and Agriculture*, **17**, 417-421.

Bogaert, C, Jouany, J P and Jeminet, G (1990) Effects of the ionophore antibiotics monensin, monensin-propionate, abierixin and calcimycin on ruminal fermentation *in vitro* (Rusitec). *Animal Feed Science and Technology*, **28**, 183-197.

Bolle, H J, Seiler, W and Bolin, B (1986) Other greenhouse gases and aerosols. Trace gases in the atmospheres. In: *The Greenhouse Effect,*

Climatic Change and Ecosystems (Scope 29) (Editors B Bolin, B O R Döös, J Jäger and R A Warrick). Wiley & Sons, Chichester, 157-203.

Bouwman, A F (1989) The role of soils and land use in the greenhouse effect. Background Paper at an International Conference on "Soils and the Greenhouse Effect", The Netherlands, 14-18 August 1989.

Bouwman, A F (1990) Land use related sources of greenhouse gases. *Land Use Policy*, **7**, 154-164.

Brasseur, G and Hitchman, M H (1988) Stratospheric response to trace gas perturbations: changes in ozone and temperature distributions. *Science*, **240**, 634-637.

Brethour, J R and Chalupa, W V (1977) Amicloral and monensin in high-roughage cattle rations. *Journal of Animal Science*, **45** (Supplement), 222.

Byers, F M (1980) Determining effects of monensin on energy value of corn silage diets for beef cattle by linear or semi-log methods. *Journal of Animal Science*, **51**, 158.

Callendar, G S (1938) The artificial production of carbon dioxide and its influence on temperature. *Quarterly Journal of the Royal Meteorological Society*, **64**, 223.

Caffarel-Mendez, S, Demuynck, C and Jeminet, G (1987) Etude *in vitro* de quelques antibiotiques ionophores et de certains de leurs dérivés. II caractérisation des propriétiés ionophores des composés dans un système modèle, pour les ions Na$^+$ et K$^+$. *Reproduction Nutrition Development*, **27**, 921-929.

Chalupa, W (1977) Manipulating rumen fermentation. *Journal of Animal Science*, **45**, 585-599.

Chalupa, W, Corbett, W and Brethour, J (1978) Manipulating rumen fermentation with monensin and amicloral. *Abstracts of the American Society of Animal Science*, **410**.

Chalupa, W (1980) Chemical control of rumen microbial metabolism. In: *Digestive Physiology and Metabolism of Ruminants* (Editors Y Ruchenbusch and P Thivend). MTP Press Ltd, Lancaster, 325-347.

Chameides, W L, Liu, S C and Cicerone, R J (1977) Possible variations in atmospheric methane. *Journal of Geophysical Research*, **82**, 1795-1798.

Chen, M and Wolin, M J (1977) Influence of methane production by *Methanobacterium ruminantium* on the fermentation of glucose and lactate by *Selenomonas ruminantium*. *Applied and Environmental Microbiology*, **34**, 756-759.

Cheng, K J, Akin, D E and Costerton, J W (1977) Rumen bacteria: interaction with particulate dietary components and response to dietary variation. *Federation Proceedings*, **36**, 193-197.

Cheng, K J, McCowan, R P and Costerton, J W (1979) Adherent epithelial bacteria in ruminants and their roles in digestive tract function. *American Journal of Clinical Nutrition*, **32**, 139-148.

Church, D C (1973) *Digestive Physiology and Nutrition of Ruminants, Volume I, Digestive Physiology.* O & B Books, Corrollis, Oregan, USA, 316 pp.

Cicerone, R J and Shetter, J D (1981) Sources of atmospheric methane: Measurements in rice paddies and a discussion. *Journal of Geophysical Research*, **86**, 7203-7209.

Cicerone, R J, Shetter, J D and Delwiche, C C (1983) Seasonal variation of methane flux from a Californian rice paddy. *Journal of Geophysical Research*, **88**, 11022-11024.

Cicerone, R J (1988) How has the atmospheric concentration of CO changed? In: *The Changing Atmosphere* (Editors F S Rowland and I S A Isaksen). John Wiley, New York, 49-61.

Cicerone, R J and Oremland, R S (1988) Biogeochemical aspects of atmospheric methane. *Global Biogeochemical Cycles*, **2**, 299-327.

Clapperton, J L (1974)   The effect of trichloroacetamide, chloroform and linseed oil given into the rumen of sheep on some of the end-products of rumen digestion. *British Journal of Nutrition*, **32**, 155-161.

Clapperton, J L (1977)   The effect of a methane-suppressing compound, trichloroethyl adipate on rumen fermentation and the growth of sheep. *Animal Production*, **24**, 169-181.

Collins, N M and Wood, T G (1984)   Termites and atmospheric gas production. *Science*, **224**, 84-86.

Craig, H and Chou, C C (1982) Methane: The record on polar ice cores. *Geophysical Research Letter*, **9**, 1221-1224.

Crutzen, P J (1987) The role of the tropics in atmospheric chemistry. In: *The Geophysiology of Amazonia* (Editor R Dickinson). Wiley, New York, 107-130.

Crutzen, P J, Aselmann, I and Seiler, W (1986)   Methane production by domestic animals, wild ruminants, other herbivorous fauna and humans. *Tellus*, **38B**, 271-284.

Czerkawski, J W, Blaxter, K L and Wainman, F W (1966a) The metabolism of oleic, linoleic, and linolenic acids by sheep with reference to their effects on methane production. *British Journal of Nutrition*, **20**, 349-362.

Czerkawski, J W, Blaxter, K L and Wainman, F W (1966b) The effect of linseed oil and of linseed oil fatty acids incorporated in the diet on the metabolism of sheep. *British Journal of Nutrition*, **20**, 485-494.

Czerkawski, J W and Breckenridge, G (1969) Fermentation of various soluble carbohydrates by rumen microorganisms with particular reference to methane production. *British Journal of Nutrition*, **23**, 925-937.

Czerkawski, J W (1969) Methane production in ruminants and its significance. *World Review of Nutrition and Dietetics*, **11**, 240-282.

Czerkawski, J W, Harfoot, C G and Breckenridge, G (1972) The relationship between methane production and concentrations of hydrogen in the aqueous and gaseous phases during rumen fermentation *in vitro*. *Journal of Applied Bacteriology*, **35**, 537-551.

Czerkawski, J W (1973) Effect of linseed oil fatty acids and linseed oil on rumen fermentation in sheep. *Journal of Agricultural Science*, **81**, 517-531.

Czerkawski, J W (1986) *An Introduction to Rumen Studies*. Pergamon Press, Oxford, 236 pp.

Daniels, L, Fulton, G, Spencer, R W and Orme-Johnson, W H (1980) Origin of hydrogen in methane produced by *Methanobacterium thermoautotrophicum*. *Journal of Bacteriology*, **141**, 694-698.

Daniels, L, Sparling, R and Dennis Sprott, G (1984) The bioenergetics of methanogenesis. *Biochimica et Biophysica Acta*, **768**, 113-163.

David, L, Leal Ayala, H, and Tabet, J C (1985) Abierixin a new polyether antibiotic. Production, structural determination, biological activities. *Journal of Antibiotics*, **38**, 1655-1663.

Davies, A, Nwaonu, H N, Stanier, G and Boyle, F T (1982) Properties of a novel series of inhibitors of rumen methanogenesis; *in vitro* and *in vivo* experiments including growth trials on 2, 4-bis (trichloromethyl)-benzo [1,3] dioxin-6-carboxylic acid. *British Journal of Nutrition*, **47**, 565-576.

Demeyer, D I and Henderickx, H K (1967a) Methane production from glucose *in vitro* by mixed rumen bacteria. *Biochemical Journal*, **105**, 271-277.

Demeyer, D I and Henderickx, H K (1967b) The effect of C_{18} unsaturated fatty acids on methane production *in vitro* by mixed rumen bacteria. *Biochimica et Biophysica Acta*, **137**, 484-497.

Demeyer, D I and Van Nevel, C J (1975) Methanogenesis an integrated part of carbohydrate fermentation and its control. In: *Digestion and Metabolism in the Ruminant* (Editors I W MacDonald and A C

Warner). The University of New England Publishing Unit, Armidale, Australia, 366-382.

Demeyer, D I (1988) *Vezelvertering bij eenmagigen K.V.I.V.T.I.* Studiedag-Genootschap Veevoeding-Veeteelt-Melle, 28 January.

De Graeve, K and Demeyer, D I (1988) Rumen and hindgut fermentation: differences for possible exploitation? *Mededelingen van de Faculteit Landbouwwetenschappen, Rijksuniversiteit Te Ghent*, **53**, 1805-1809.

Donner, L and Ramanathan, V (1980) Methane and nitrous oxide: their effect on the terrestrial climate. *Journal of Atmospheric Science*, **37**, 119-124.

Dowd, R M (1986) The greenhouse effect. *Environmental Science and Technology*, **20**, 767.

Eadie, J M, Hyldgaard-Jensen, J, Mann, S O, Reid, R S and Whitelaw, F G (1970) Observations on the microbiology and biochemistry of the rumen in cattle given different quantities of a pelleted barley ration. *British Journal of Nutrition*, **24**, 157-177.

Ehhalt, D H (1974) The atmospheric cycle of methane. *Tellus*, **26**, 58-70.

Flatt, W P, Moe, P W, Moore, L A, Hooven, N W, Lehman, R P, Ørskov, E R and Hemken, R W (1969) Energy utilisation by high producing dairy cows. I. Experimental design, ration composition, digestibility data and animal performance during energy balance trials. In: *Energy Metabolism of Farm Animals* (Editors K L Blaxter, J Kielanowski and G Thorbek). Oriel Press, Newcastle upon Tyne, 221-234.

Fraser, P J, Rasmussen, R A, Creffield, J W, French, J R and Khalil, M A K (1986) Termites and global methane - another assessment. *Journal of Atmospheric Chemistry*, **4**, 295-310.

Gaboyard, C (1987) *Etude de dérivés des antibiotiques ionophores monensine, lonomycine, cationomycine complexation de Na$^+$ et K$^+$*, toxicité, activité anticoccidienne et facteur de croissance. Thèse de Docteur

Ingénieur. Ecole de Chimie, University Blaize Pascal, Clermont-Ferrand.

Glass, T L, Bryant, M P and Wolin, M J (1977) Partial purification of ferredoxin from *Ruminococcus albus* and its role in pyruvate metabolism and reduction of nicotinamide adenine dinucleotide by H_2. *Journal of Bacteriology*, **131**, 463-472.

Gribbin, J (1988) The greenhouse effect. *New Scientist*, **120**, No. 1635, 1-4.

Gunsalus, R P, Romesser, J A and Wolfe, R S (1978) Preparation of coenzyme M analogues and their activity in the methyl-coenzyme M reductase system of *Methanobacterium thermoautotrophicum*. *Biochemistry*, **17**, 2374-2377.

Harris, J E, Evans, D M, Knox, M R and Archer, D B (1987) Genetic approaches with methanogens important in mesophilic anaerobic digestion. In: *Recent Advances in Anaerobic Bacteriology* (Editors S P Boriello and J M Hardie). Martinus Nnijhor, Dordrecht, 123-137.

Hillman, K, Lloyd, D and Williams, A G (1988) Interactions between the methanogen *Methanosarcina barkeri* and rumen holotrich ciliate protozoa. *Letters in Applied Microbiology*, **7**, 49-53.

Hobson, P N (1972) Physiological characteristics of rumen microbes and relation to diet and fermentation patterns. *Proceedings of the Nutrition Society*, **31**, 135-141.

Holzapfal-Pschorn, A and Seiler W (1986) Methane emission during a cultivation period from Italian rice paddy. *Journal of Geophysical Research*, **91**, 11803-11814.

Horton, G M J, Bassendowski, K A and Keeler, E H (1979) Feed utilisation and performance of steers fed monensin and amicloral. *Abstracts of the American Society of Animal Science*, **376**.

Horton, G M J (1980) A note on the effect of monensin and amichloral in steer diets. *Animal Production*, **30**, 441-444.

Houston, D C (1979) The adaptions of scavengers. In: *Serengeti Dynamics of an Ecosystem* (Editors A R E Sinclair and M Norton-Griffith). University of Chicago Press, Chicago - London, 263-286.

Hungate, R E (1963) *Symposia of the Society for General Microbiology*, 8, 266-297.

Hungate, R E (1966) *The Rumen and Its Microbes*. Academic Press, New York, 533 pp.

Hungate, R E (1967) Hydrogen as an intermediate in the rumen fermentation. *Archiv Fur Mikrobiologie*, 59, 158-161.

Hungate, R E, Smith, W, Bauchop, T, Yu, I and Rabinowitz, J C (1970) Formate as an intermediate in the bovine rumen fermentation. *Journal of Bacteriology*, 102, 389-397.

Huster, R, Gilles, H and Thauer, R K (1985) Is coenzyme M bound to factor F_{430} in methanogenic bacteria? *European Journal of Biochemistry*, 148, 107-111.

Isaksen, I S A and Hov, O (1987) Calculation of trends in the tropospheric concentration of O_3, OH, CH_4 and NO_x. *Tellus*, 39B, 271-285.

Itabashi, H, Kobayashi, T and Matsumoto, M (1984) The effects of rumen ciliate protozoa on energy metabolism and some constituents in rumen fluid and blood plasma of goats. *Japanese Journal of Zootechnical Science*, 55, 248-256.

Iversen, N, Oremland, R S and Klug, M J (1987) Big Soda Lake (Nevada), 3, Pelagic methanogenesis and anaerobic methane oxidation. *Limnology and Oceanography*, 32, 804-814.

Jacobs, N J and Wolin, M J (1963) *Biochimica et Biophysica Acta*, 69, 18-21.

Jones, W J, Nagle, D P and Whitman, W B (1987) Methanogens and the diversity of *Archaebacteria. Microbiological Review*, 51, 135-177

Kenealy, W R and Zeikus, J G (1982) One-carbon metabolism in methanogenes: Evidence for synthesis of a two-carbon cellular intermediate and unification of catabolism and anabolism in *Methanosarcina barkeri*. *Journal of Bacteriology*, **151**, 932-941.

Khalil, M A K and Rasmussen, R A (1983) Sources, sinks and seasonal cycles of atmospheric methane. *Journal of Geophysical Research*, **88**, 5131-5144.

Kone, P, Machado, P F and Cook, R M (1989) Effect of the combination of monensin and isoacids on rumen fermentation *in vitro*. *Journal of Dairy Science*, **72**, 2767-2771.

Koyama, T (1964) Biogeochemical studies on lake sediments and paddy soils and the production of hydrogen and methane. In: *Recent Researches in the Fields of Hydrosphere Atmosphere and Geochemistry* (Editors T Miyake and T Koyama). Maruzen, Tokyo, 143-177.

Kreuzer, M, Kirchgessner, M and Muller, H L (1986) Effect of defaunation on the loss of energy in wethers fed different quantities of cellulose and normal or steamflaked maize starch. *Animal Feed Science and Technology*, **16**, 233-241.

Kriss, M (1930) Quantitative relations of dry matter of food consumed, heat production and gaseous outgo and the insensible loss in bodyweight of cattle. *Journal of Agricultural Research*, **40**, 283.

Krumholz, L R, Forsberg, C W and Veira, D M (1983) Association of methanogenic bacteria with rumen protozoa. *Canadian Journal of Microbiology*, **29**, 676-680.

Krzycki, J and Zeikus, J G (1980) Quantification of corrinoids in methanogenic bacteria. *Current Microbiology*, **3**, 243-245.

Kvenvolden, K (1989) Methane hydrates and global climate. *Global Biogeochemical Cycles*, **2**, 221-229.

Lanigan, G W, Payne, A L and Peterson, J E (1978) Antimethanogenic drugs and *Heliotropium europium* poisoning in penned sheep. *Australian Journal of Agricultural Research*, **29**, 1281-1292.

Latham, M J and Wolin, M J (1977) Fermentation of cellulose by *Ruminococcus flavefaciens* in the presence and absence of *Methanobacterium ruminantium*. *Applied and Environmental Microbiology*, **34**, 297-301.

Leng, R A (1970) Formation and production of volatile fatty acids in the rumen. In: *Physiology of Digestion and Metabolism in the Ruminant* (Editor A T Phillipson). Oriel Press, Newcastle upon Tyne, 406-421.

Liu, C M (1982) Microbial aspects of polyether antibiotics: activity, production and biosynthesis. In: *Polyether Antibiotics Naturally Occurring Acid Ionophores. Volume 1: Biology* (Editor J W Westley). Marcel Dekker, New York, 43-102.

Logan, J A, Prather, M J, Wofsy, S C and McElroy, M B (1981) Tropospheric chemistry: A global perspective. *Journal of Geophysical Research*, **86**, 7210-7254.

Lovelock, J E and Margulis, L (1974) Atmospheric homeostasis by and for the biosphere: The Gaia Hypothesis. *Tellus*, **26**, 1-10.

Lovley, D R and Klug, M J (1983) Sulphate reducers can out compete methanogens at freshwater sulphate concentration. *Applied Environmental Microbiology*, **45**, 187-192.

MacRae, J C and Lobley, G E (1982) Some factors influencing thermal energy losses during the metabolism of ruminants. *Livestock Production Science*, **9**, 447-456.

Mah, R A, Ward, D M, Baresi, L and Glass, T L (1977) Biogenesis of methane. *Annual Reviews of Microbiology*, **31**, 309-341.

Marland, G and Rotty, R M (1984) Carbon dioxide emissions from fossil fuels. A procedure for estimation and results for 1950-1982. *Tellus*, **36B**, 232-261.

Martin, S A and Macy, J M (1985) Effects of monensin pyromellitic diimide and 2-bromoethanesulphonic acid on rumen fermentation *in vitro*. *Journal of Animal Science*, **60**, 544-550.

Marty, R J and Demeyer, D I (1973) The effect of inhibitors of methane production on fermentation pattern and stoichiometry *in vitro* using rumen contents from sheep fed molasses. *British Journal of Nutrition*, **30**, 369-376.

Mathers, J C and Miller, E L (1982) Some effects of chloral hydrate on rumen fermentation and digestion in sheep. *Journal of Agricultural Science*, **99**, 215-224.

Matthews, E and Fung, I (1987) Methane emission from natural wetlands: Global distribution, area and environmental characteristics of sources. *Global Biogeochemical Cycles*, **1**, 61-86.

McBride, B C and Wolfe, R S (1971) Biochemistry of methane formation. *Advanced Chemical Series*, **105**, 11-22.

Migeotte, M J (1948) Spectroscopic evidence of methane in the earth's atmosphere. *Physical Reviews*, **73**, 519-520.

Miller, T L, Wolin, M J, Hongxue, Z and Bryant, M P (1986) Characteristics of methanogens isolated from bovine rumen. *Applied Environmental Microbiology*, **51**, 201-202.

Ministry of Agriculture, Fisheries and Food (1989) *Agricultural and Horticultural Returns - Final Results of the June 1988 Census in England and Wales*. HMSO, London, 9-15.

Moe, P W and Tyrrell, H F (1979) Methane production in dairy cows. *Journal of Dairy Science*, **62**, 1583-1586.

Molina, M J and Rowland, F S (1974) Stratospheric sink for chlorofluoromethanes: Chlorine catalyzed destruction of ozone. *Nature*, **249**, 810-812.

Moomaw, C R and Hungate, R E (1963) Ethanol conversion in the rumen. *Journal Bacteriology*, **85**, 721-722.

Nicholson, J W G and Sutton, J D (1971) Some effects of unsaturated oils given to dairy cows with rations of different roughage content. *Journal of Dairy Research*, **38**, 363-372.

Opperman, R A, Nelson, W O and Brown, R E (1957) *In vitro* studies on methanogenic rumen bacteria. *Journal of Dairy Science*, **40**, 779-788.

Oremland, R S (1979) Methanogenic activity in plankton samples and fish intestines: A mechanism for in situ methanogenesis in oceanic surface waters. *Limnology and Oceanography*, **24**, 1136-1141.

Orpin, C G (1979) Association of rumen ciliate protozoa with plant particles *in vitro*. *Society for General Microbiology Quarterly*, **7**, 31-32.

Ørskov, E R and Allen, D M (1966) Utilisation of salts of volatile fatty acids by growing sheep. *British Journal of Nutrition*, **20**, 509-534.

Ørskov, E R, Flatt, W P and Moe, P W (1968) Fermentation balance approach to estimate extent of fermentation and efficiency of volatile fatty acid formation in ruminants. *Journal of Dairy Science*, **51**, 1429-1435.

Ørskov, E R, Grub, D A, Smith, J S, Webster, A J F and Corrigall, W (1979) Efficiency of utilisation of volatile fatty acids for maintenance and energy retention of sheep. *British Journal of Nutrition*, **41**, 541-551.

Patterson, J A and Hespell, R B (1979) Trimethylamine and methylamine as growth substrates for rumen bacteria and *Methanosarcina barkeri*. *Current Microbiology*, **3**, 79-83.

Paynter, M J B and Hungate, R E (1968) Characterisation of *Methanobacterium mobilis* sp.n., isolated from the bovine rumen. *Journal of Bacteriology*, **95**, 1943-1951.

Pearce, F (1989) Methane: the hidden greenhouse gas. *New Scientist*, **122**, No 1663, 37-41.

Pond, W G (1985) Advances in swine nutrition. *Cornell Veterinarian,* 75, 201.

Pressman, B C (1976) Biological applications of ionophores. *Annual Reviews of Biochemistry,* 45, 501-530.

Prins, R A and Lankhorst, A (1977) Synthesis of acetate from CO_2 in the caecum of some rodents. *FEMS Microbiology Letters,* 1, 255-258.

Prins, R A (1977) Biochemical activities of gut microorganisms In: *Microbial Ecology of the Gut* (Editors R T J Clarke and T Bauchop). Academic Press, London, 73-183.

Prins, R A (1978) Nutritional impact of intestinal drug-microbe interactions. In: *Nutrition and Drug Interrelationships.* Academic Press, New York, 189-251.

Ramanathan, V (1975) Greenhouse effect due to chlorofluorocarbons: climatic implications, *Science,* 190, 50-52.

Ramanathan, V, Cicerone, R J, Singh, H B and Kiehl, J T (1985) Trace gas trends and their potential role in climate change. *Journal of Geophysical Research,* 90, 5547- 5566.

Rasmussen, R A and Khalil, M A K (1984) Atmospheric methane in the recent and ancient atmospheres: Concentrations trends and interhemispheric gradient. *Journal of Geophysical Research,* 89, 11599-11605.

Raun, A P, Cooley, C O, Potter, E P, Rathmacher, R P and Richardson, L F (1976) Effect of monensin on feed efficiency of feed-lot cattle. *Journal of Animal Science,* 43, 670-677.

Reed, P W and Lardy, H A (1972) A 23187: a divalent cation ionophore. *Journal of Biological Chemistry,* 247, 6970-6977.

Ridley, B A, Carroll, M A and Gregory, G L (1987) Measurements of nitric oxide in the boundary layer and free troposphere over the Pacific Ocean. *Journal of Geophysical Research,* 92, 2025-2047.

Robbins, R C, Cavanagh, L A, Salas, L J and Robinson, E (1973) Analysis of ancient atmospheres. *Journal of Geophysical Research*, **78**, 5341-5344.

Rodhe, H (1990) A comparison of the contribution of various gases to the greenhouse effect. *Science*, **248**, 1217-1219.

Romatowski, J (1979) *Mechanism of Action of Monensin in the Rumen*. M S Thesis, University of Delaware, Newark, USA.

Rowe, J, Loughnan, M L, Nolan, J V and Leng, R A (1979) Secondary fermentation in the rumen of a sheep given a diet based on molasses. *British Journal of Nutrition*, **41**, 393-397.

Russell, J B and Martin, S A (1984) Effects of various methane inhibitors on the fermentation of amino acids by mixed rumen microorganisms *in vitro*. *Journal of Animal Science*, **59**, 1329-1338.

Safley, L M, Casada, M E, Woodbury, J W and Roos, K F (1992) *Global Methane Emissions from Livestock and Poultry Manure*. Environmental Protection Agency, USA, 1-5.

Schwartz, H M and Gilchrist, F M C (1975) Microbial interactions with the diet and the host animal. In: *Digestion and Metabolism in the Ruminant* (Editors I W McDonald and A C I Warner). New England Publishing Unit, Armidale, Australia, 165-179.

Seiler, W (1984) Contribution of biological processes to the global budget of methane in the atmosphere. In: *Current Perspectives in Microbial Ecology* (Editors M J Klug and C A Reddy). American Society for Microbiology, Washington D C, 468-477.

Seiler, W, Holzapfal-Pschorn, A, Conrad, R and Scharffe, D (1984) Methane emission from rice paddies. *Journal of Atmospheric Chemistry*, **1**, 241-268.

Seiler, W, Conrad, R and Scharffe, D (1984) Field studies of methane emission from termite nests in to the atmosphere and measurements of methane uptake by tropical soils. *Journal of Atmospheric Chemistry*, **1**, 171-186.

Shapiro, S (1982) Do Corrinoids function in the methanogenic dissimilation of methanol by *Methanosarcina barkeri*. *Canadian Journal of Microbiology*, **28**, 629-635.

Sheppard, J C, Westberg, H, Hopper, J F, Ganesea, K and Zimmerman, P (1982) Inventory of global methane sources and their production rates. *Journal of Geophysical Research*, **87**, 1305-1312.

Smith, P H and Hungate, R E (1958) Isolation and characterisation of *Methanobacterium ruminantium* n. sp. *Journal of Bacteriology*, **75**, 713-718.

Sowers, K R and Ferry, J G (1983) Isolation and characterization of a methylotrophic marine methanogen, *Methanococcoides methylutens*. *Applied Environmental Microbiology*, **45**, 5-11.

Stumm, C K, Gijzen, H J and Vogels, G D (1982) Association of methanogenic bacteria with ovine rumen ciliates. *British Journal of Nutrition*, **47**, 95-99.

Stupperich, E, Hammel, K E, Fuchs, G and Thauer, R K (1983) Carbon monoxide fixation into the carboxyl group of acetyl coenzyme A during autotrophic growth of *Methanobacterium thermoautotrophicum*. *FEBS Letters*, **152**, 21-23.

Swift, R W, Bratzler, J W, James, W H, Tillman, A D and Meek, D C (1948) Effect of dietary fat on utilisation of energy and protein of rations by sheep. *Journal of Animal Science*, **7**, 475.

Svensson, B H (1984) Different temperature optima for methane formation when enrichments from acid peat are supplemented with acetate or hydrogen. *Applied Environmental Microbiology*, **48**, 389-394.

Taylor, C D and Wolfe, R S (1974) A simplified assay for coenzyme M ($HSCH_3CH_2SO_3$). Resolution of methylcobalamin-coenzyme M methyltransferase and use of sodium borohydride. *Journal of Biological Chemistry*, **249**, 4886-4890.

Thauer, R K, Jungermann, K and Decker, K (1977) Energy conservation in chemotrophic anaerobic bacteria. *Bacteriology Reviews*, **41**, 100-180.

Thomas, P C and Clapperton, J L (1972) Significance to the host of changes in fermentation activity. *Proceedings of the Nutrition Society*, **31**, 165-170.

Thomson, F and Lamming, G E (1972) The flow of digesta dry matter and starch to the duodenum in sheep given rations containing straw of varying particle size. *British Journal of Nutrition*, **28**, 391-403.

Thompson, A M and Cicerone, R J (1986) Possible perturbations to atmospheric CO, CH_4 and OH. *Journal of Geophysical Research*, **91**, 10853-10864.

Ulyatt, M J, Bellow, D W, Reid, C S W and Bauchop, T (1975) Structure and function of the large intestine of ruminants. In: *Digestion and Metabolism in the Ruminant* (Editors I W McDonald and A C I Warner). University of New England Publication Unit, Armidale, Australia.

Wallace, R J, Cheng, K-J, Dinsdale, D and Ørskov, E R (1979) An independent microbial flora of the epithelium and its role in the ecomicrobiology of the rumen. *Nature*, **279**, 424-426.

Walsh, C, Jacobson, F and Ryerson, C C (1980) Flavine coenzyme analogs as probes of flavo enzyme reaction mechanisms. In: *Biomimetic Chemistry, Advanced Chemistry Series*, **191**, 119-138.

Wang, W C, Young, Y L, Lacis, A A, Mo, T and Hansen, J E (1976) Greenhouse effects due to man-made perturbations of trace gases. *Science*, **194**, 685-690.

Ward, D M and Olson, G J (1980) Terminal processes in anaerobic degradation of an algal-bacterial mat in a high sulphate hot spring. *Applied Environmental Microbiology*, **40**, 67-74.

103

Warner, A C I (1962) Enumeration of rumen microorganisms. *Journal of General Microbiology*, **28**, 119-128.

Warrick, R (1990) The greenhouse effect and climatic change. Agricultural Group Symposium Industry, Agriculture and the Atmosphere, 23 January 1990. *Journal of the Science of Food and Agriculture*, **53**, 420-421.

Warrick, R A and Barrow, E M (1990) Climate and Sea Level Change: A Perspective. *Outlook on Agriculture*, **19**, 5-8.

Wedegaertner, T C and Johnson, D E (1983) Monensin effects on digestibility, methanogenesis and heat increment of a cracked corn-silage diet fed to steers. *Journal of Animal Science*, **57**, 168-177.

Weiss, R F (1981) The temporal and spatial distribution of tropospheric nitrous oxide. *Journal of Geophysical Research*, **86**, 7185-7195.

Weller, R A, Gray, F V and Pilgrim, A F (1958) The conversion of plant nitrogen to microbial nitrogen in the rumen of the sheep. *British Journal of Nutrition*, **12**, 421-429.

Whitelaw, F G, Eadie, J M, Bruce, L A and Shand, W J (1984) Methane formation in faunated and ciliate-free cattle and its relationship with rumen volatile fatty acid proportions. *British Journal of Nutrition*, **52**, 261-275.

Williams, A G (1986) Rumen holotrich ciliate protozoa. *Microbiological Reviews*, **50**, 25-49.

Wolin, M J A (1960) A theoretical rumen fermentation balance. *Journal of Dairy Science*, **43**, 1452-1463.

Wolin, M J A (1981) Fermentation in the rumen and human large intestine. *Science*, **213**, 1463-1468.

Wolin, M J A (1982) Hydrogen transfer in microbial communities. In: *Microbial Interactions and Communities, Volume 1* (Editors A T Bull and J H Slater). Academic, San Diego, California, 323-356.

Wolin, M J A and Miller, T L (1988) Microbe-microbe interactions. In: *The Rumen Microbial Ecosystem* (Editor P N Hobson). Elsevier Applied Science, London, 343-359.

World Meteorological Organisation (WMO) (1986) Report of the International Conference on the Assessment of the Role of Carbon Dioxide and of Other Greenhouse Gases in Climate Variations and Associated Impacts. Villach, Austria, 9-15 October 1985. WMO - No. 661, WMO, Geneva.

Zimmermann, P R, Greenberg, J P, Wandiga, S O and Crutzen, P J (1982) Termites: a potentially large source of atmospheric methane, carbon dioxide and molecular hydrogen. *Science*, **218**, 563-565.